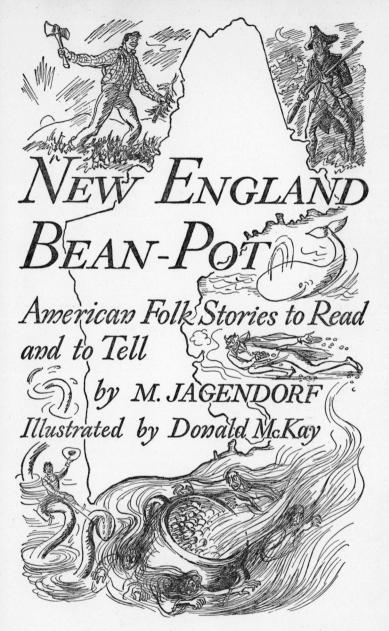

NEW ENGLAND BEAN-POT

American Folk Stories to Read and to Tell

by M. JAGENDORF

Illustrated by Donald McKay

INTRODUCTION BY B. A. BOTKIN

THE VANGUARD PRESS, INC. NEW YORK

Second Printing

BOOKS BY M. JAGENDORF

PROSE

New England Bean-Pot   **747886**
Tyll Ulenspiegel's Merry Pranks
A World of Stories for Children (IN COLLABORATION WITH
    BARRETT CLARK)
In the Days of the Han

PLAYS

Penny Puppets, Penny Theatre and Penny Plays
One-Act Plays for Young Folks
Pantomimes for the Children's Theatre
Fairyland and Footlights
Nine Short Plays
Around America with the Indians (IN COLLABORATION
    WITH NINA B. LAMKIN)
Plays for Club, School, and Camp
Buffalmacco's Jest
The Pie and the Tart (ADAPTATIONS)
The Farce of Pierre Patelin
The Cave of Salamance
Jeppe of the Hills
The Pastrybaker
Twenty-Five Non-Royalty Plays for Children (ANTHOLOGY)
Twenty-Five Non-Royalty Holiday Plays
Twenty Non-Royalty Mystery Plays
Twenty Non-Royalty Ghost Plays

IN PREPARATION

Folkstories from the Middle States
Folkstories from the Southern States
Folkstories from the Western States

This book is dedicated to the members
of the National Story League in our land
who carry on the ancient art of storytelling

For the Reader

EXCITING TALES, good yarns, merry jokes, clever hoaxes, ghost stories, spiced anecdotes are experiences of adventure and pleasure in the life of folk, people—you and I.

When they are told over and over again for many years, they become folklore.

Folklore, folk tales, may begin with something that really happened to some folk in the country, on the farm, woods, or fields. Or it may be something that happened in the city or on the sea—anywhere. Again, folklore and folk tales grow out of incidents in nature, or historical facts; incidents about animals, or even about objects like tables or houses or trees.

Sometimes smart folk make up a strange tale or a funny story and say it happened to them or someone they know or knew, and it becomes folklore, a folk tale.

These tales spread—they are told to friends and they in turn tell them to their friends. As they are repeated by different folk they change a little, for each one tells them in a different way, often adding something to them. In the spreading to different parts of the land each locality often claims them as their own.

There are thousands and thousands of these folk tales, legends, incidents, yarns, and anecdotes about the Indians and white settlers. Those of the settlers have grown and are still growing with the people who came, and are still coming, to America—white, black, and yellow. Spaniards, Englishmen, Irish, Germans, Poles, Italians, Swedes —peoples from every part of the world came here with high hopes and great courage. They brought with them the rich folklore of their lands, melting it together and adding it to the new, rich American lore that was coming up everywhere, in every state, with the moving years.

Thus there is not a city or hamlet, road or lane, shack or house, woods or stream, and the ocean all around us, that is not honeycombed with tales.

Since folk tales, yarns, and legends are mainly heard by word of mouth, they are known mostly in the particular place where they are told. Many of them are written down in little-known old records which very, very few people read. That is a great loss, for many of them are so delightful, so funny, so rich—they tell so much about life and people—that I am sure everyone in every part of America should, and would, like to hear them.

From this vast treasury of our lore heard and read, I have taken choice bits and set them down in story form. I call them *Folk Stories*.

They are legends, tales, yarns, jokes, incidents arranged as *Folk Stories* to read and tell. For that reason they are salted with folksayings and larded with side-lights of the localities from where they come. I have added proverbs, customs, and weather lore, and sometimes even local happenings from where the stories take place. And just as I have seen tellers of tales take pleasure spinning and garnishing their yarns for my enjoyment, so have I written these stories for you to enjoy. They are *Folk Stories* woven from the woof and warp of folk material, whether heard by word of mouth or found in old records of counties, towns, churches, or lives about people—folk like you and me.

In Maine or Massachusetts, Vermont or Connecticut, Rhode Island or New Hampshire, there is no dish better liked than brick-brown beans baked in a pot. I heard so many of the stories told in this book with the tangy, sweet-spiced taste of them in my mouth that I could think of no better title for the book than

New England Bean-Pot.

MORITZ JAGENDORF

Old Cole Farm
August, 1948

Contents

Illustrations

Foreword

A WORLD TRAVELER in folk tales, Moritz Jagendorf has come home, not to roost, but to start on a folk-tale journey around these storied United States. Naturally, and wisely, he has chosen to begin with New England—the homeland of American chimney-corner storytelling. In the days before magazines and daily newspapers, according to Harriet Beecher Stowe, "the aged told their stories to the young—tales of early life; tales of war and adventure, of forest-days, of Indian captivities and escapes, of bears and wild-cats and panthers, of rattlesnakes, of witches and wizards, and strange and wonderful dreams and appearances and providences" all by the light of the flickering hearth-fire.

Because chimney-corner storytelling has gone the way of chimney corners, surviving only in children's story hours, Dr. Jagendorf has bagged forty-six tales of the kinds enumerated, as a memorial of the good old days and good old story ways. He has recaptured the spirit of faith and wonder in which tales like these were originally told and heard. Not only the shifting firelight but the warm sunlight and the pale moonlight and the light that never was on land or sea play over them.

He has succeeded in doing this because he loves a good tale as he loves a good wine, for its body and flavor. Tales of heroism, wisdom, and mirth, telling how "most men fought hard for their freedom, many loved good learning, and some acted silly." Tales full of good talk, of good old Yankee words and sayings, of tripping phrases and cadences that roll like breakers on the shore.

He has succeeded, too, because he knows that there are as many ways of telling a story as there are ways to skin a cat. But above all because he knows that the best stories are those that are told aloud or as if told aloud, in the gollywhumping, barrel-thumping style of village store, cracker-barrel storytellers. He also knows that the best stories, like the best fish in the sea, are the ones that got away. And he has gone fishing in many an out-of-the-way, obscure source, in folk-say and book-say.

He knows that stories are not made but grow, and never stop growing. They grow in this collection as they grow in tradition, starting with an anecdote, a character, a saying, taking on form and scope, adding new details, and combining plots. "The tale spread far and wide," as he says. "I heard it once, I heard it twice, and now you've heard it, too."

B. A. BOTKIN

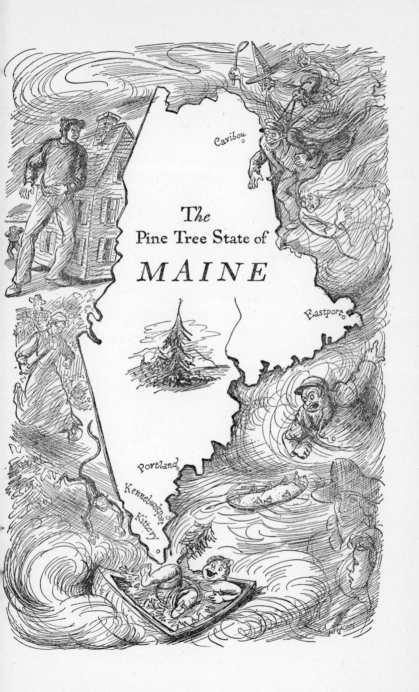

The
Pine Tree State of
MAINE

Caribou

Eastport

Portland

Kennebunkport

Kittery

Young Paul

THIS is how it began. Up in Maine the sun shone hot to warm grasshoppers, the wind whooped in the forest wild as windigos, the animals rushed over grass and leaves, and the trees bent down low to the ground. All this to welcome babe Paul, three-weeks-old babe Paul Bunyan, already big as a big Maine Man sleeping peacefully on a bed of leaves. They knew he'd be the greatest logger boss in the world. They knew he'd cut more than any man the sharp-smelling pine and spruce to race down the swollen rivers for to build cities of long, big, broad America.

Of a sudden a bright green dragonfly, the devil's darning needle, buzzed along his nose, along his eyes to tie them tight, as devil's darning needles always do. That awoke the little fellow. He opened his great, dark eyes and sneezed so strong, the white clouds in the sky were torn to shreds and flew clear to California. But he wasn't full awake yet, so he swung his dimply arms wildly all around, breaking pines and fences; then he rolled right

3

and left, aft and fore, crashing trees and boulders full four acres around. That hurt a little and made him hungry, so he raised his voice and cried loud as giant buzz-saws, for food and drink.

Pa and Ma Bunyan ran up to find out what all the rumpus was about. They learned it quickly and fed him rich brown beans from the iron bean-pot and creamy milk from sleek brown and white cows. When he was eating quietly so you could only hear him a mile or so away, Ma and Pa Bunyan began talking.

Said Pa Bunyan:

"That chunk of a feller ain't small potatoes. He's stronger 'n ten bears, an' we jest can't let 'm destroy all the trees o' Maine. Maybe if he's baptized proper he'll stop. We got ter do sumpin'!"

"I know he'll be a good little fellow if God's words is spoken over him, but I need a week afore I kin make ready for the baptism."

"That boy kin do lots o' trouble in one week, that Paul."

Ma Bunyan, she agreed, but, like the smart woman she was, she had a plan out of her head all ready.

"You make a cradle and put it in the sea, an' that'll be a fine place for my little son. The waves'll do the rockin' an' keep 'm quiet. That'll make him the salt o' the sea jest as he's the salt o' the earth."

Pa Bunyan picked out the tallest pine in all the State of Maine and cut it down. The gray clouds on high were mighty glad of that, for they always had to go around that tree when traveling in the sky.

Then Pa Bunyan chopped and hollowed and hollowed and chopped till he had a cradle round and smooth. Ma Bunyan filled it with tangy-smelling pine needles, they put the little fellow in, floated him to Eastport Bay, and anchored it strong so it wouldn't come loose.

Now little Paul had never been on the water before, and he just loved the rolling and dipping of the waves. He got hold of both sides of the cradle and began rocking it. Then a little squall came along, kind of playful, and Paul had a gollywhumping time. Soon the swells were rising and raging and going and coming the like had never been seen around the Maine coast, and that's a fact. Some of that salt spray near reached the clouds in the sky, and the waves even went as far as the Bay of Fundy. Whole villages along the coast floated in the water, and people were screaming for the billows to stop so they could stay on land, but little Paul had gone to sleep.

While he was sleeping sound and sweet in the bay, the British Navy, riding the sea, was wide awake. They heard the screaming and sent great sailing warships to see what was wrong. The ships sailed along the Maine coast until they came to the tidal waves made by little Paul's rocking cradle, and they couldn't go ahead. So they began shooting broadsides to warn him to get out of the bay. Boom! Boom! Boom! Boom! the cannons roared—seven long hours. Then the little fellow awoke and leaped out of the cradle, for he'd had enough of the sea and wanted to get back to the land, to the woods where he truly belonged.

When he jumped in the water he raised the waves so high and strong they just smashed the seven sailing British warships into a million splinters. But little Paul didn't care about this one bit.

He crawled back to the green summer forest among the pine and spruce while the poor redcoats took little Paul's cradle to build new warships.

Said Ma Bunyan:

"Pa, you was right. The little fellow's makin' lots o' trouble; we got to baptize him quick."

"Oui, we must do that," said Pa Bunyan.

So they took little Paul to the largest bay along the coast to baptize him right and proper. But before they could do it they had to build a crane in which to hoist him into the water.

Sunday came, and Pa and Ma Bunyan brought the boy proudly in a great wagon drawn by thirty-two oxen. Most of the people of Maine came, and those in Canada who lived along the border. They all came to the christening party of little Paul.

They ate and made merry, and so did Paul, until the red sun rolled down in the sky. Then they hoisted him high in the crane for to be baptized in the bay. When they got him halfway, the iron chain broke and the boy fell, Kerplunk! into the water. He hit it so hard that he started a new tidal wave that reached the Bay of Fundy and has never stopped to this very day.

But little Paul was baptized just the same and raised no rumpus after that. He grew bigger and stronger and did great deeds without end just as the waves he began kept on going without end.

The Skipper and the Witch

IN Kittery by the sea, lived Skipper Perkins, who squeezed pennies so the eagles screamed for he trusted neither man nor God—only money. His face was hard, and his lips were tight, and he was far from a pleasant sight.

And in Kittery by the sea, lived tall Betty Booker, who slept with her head in Kittery town and her feet in York that was miles away. Her hair was wild and gray, her nose sharp as a hawk's, and her eyes like darting snakes. At night she flew over sea and land, but when the sun was up she stomped around prying into business that was none of her own.

One day she met Skipper Perkins walking to the wharf to set his boat a-sailing for a catch.

"Skipper Perkins, Skipper Perkins, bring a poor old woman a bit o' hal'but when you come back. It don't have to be big, it don't have to be small, just 'nuf for me to keep body 'n' bones t'gether."

8

"Show me your money, ma'am; I don' sail my schooner fishin' without gettin' paid for my fish."

Betty Booker shook her wild gray hair.

"You're a rich man, Skipper Perkins, and you'll never miss a bit o' hal'but in your great catch the sea gives you free. I got no money, Skipper Perkins."

"Away wi' ye, old woman wi' the evil eyes. No hal'but ye'll get from me without payin' for it."

The Skipper and his men set out in the boat on the gray sea, and Betty Booker mumbled words in the wind none could hear.

Never was there sadder sailing of a schooner from Maine. The second day out half the crew got sick; the third, a gale pounded and tossed and whistled a thousand tunes. It beat the boat and tore the sails, it ripped the mast and near splintered the planks. No fish ever came near Skipper Perkins' trawls. Day after day there was only bad luck till Skipper Perkins had to come back a poorer man than he set out.

His face was drawn, his eyes were small, and his mouth was tight. Few spoke to him, and he spoke to fewer.

One day he saw Betty Booker, and he gave her a wide berth, but she ran after him and cried:

"Skipper Perkins, hope you're more kind to old women than you were to me. Don't grudge 'em a bit o' fish when you come in wi' a boatful of 'em."

"Away wi' ye, ye old witch! I'd be kind to ye and burn ye on a slow fire, for the witch ye are."

"You've a hard heart, Skipper. It still needs a little softenin', it needs a little softenin'."

She laughed loud and shrill, and Skipper Perkins walked as fast as his legs would go.

From that day on the Skipper never dared to go out in the dark, for he heard Old Betty Booker was busy making a witch-bridle to ride him to York for to teach him kindness.

And so she was. Every night Betty Booker sat in her hut busy making a witch-bridle. She took black hair from the tail of a horse standing in his stall, she took strands from tows lying around fishers' wharves, and she took the inside bark from yellow birch in the dark woods. She took all these and wove and stitched and stitched and wove till she had the finest witch-bridle ever made on the coast of Maine. Then she sent word to the Skipper she was coming for him to break his evil temper in a fierce wild ride.

Skipper Perkins, white with fear, barred his door and on stormy nights piled beds and tables against it. But one wild night, when the winds screeched and the squalls pounded, all the bars and all the bedding and tables and chairs and his own strong shoulders against the door did little good.

First the wind stormed against the hinges, but the door held strong; then the rain and squalls came to help, and the door held strong. But through it came a screeching voice:

"Bring a poor woman a bit o' hal'but, bring a poor

woman a bit o' hal'but, Skipper Perkins," and there was pounding and beating at the door worse than ever before.

The Skipper felt hot and cold, and salty perspiration ran down his face and back. He braced his shoulders against the wood and his boots against the floor beams to hold the door.

"It's easier t' give a poor old woman a bit o' hal'but than holdin' the door," screeched Betty Booker, while the gale grew wilder, the wind screeched fiercer, and the rain pounded harder.

The door opened a little bit; then rain, wind, and witches pushed harder, and it opened a little more, while the Skipper slid along the slippery floor.

Betty Booker and her familiars raced in through the crack, chattering, screeching, throwing things wherever they would go.

The Skipper leaped on the bed winding his sheets around him, but it did little good. The witches fell on him and tore his clothes to shreds, and Old Betty Booker put on him the fine new witch-bridle. Then she leaped into the saddle, and the rest of the witches leaped on her. Whee!!! they were off through wind and rain, through thunder and lightning.

They rode high, they rode low, they rode far, they rode wide. Skipper Perkins couldn't rest a breath, for, when he tried, sharp claws dug into his sides, and Betty Booker screamed:

"Remember, Skipper Perkins! Remember to be kind

to a poor old woman when she begs for a bit o' hal'but. Don't ask for money when she ain't got none. Just be kind an' don't grudge a bit o' what you have so much." The rest of the witches kept chorus to that song.

So they rode into York and all around, and the first break of dawn they rode back to Kittery and left Skipper Perkins inside the broken door.

For weeks Skipper Perkins stayed in bed to heal the wounds of that mad night, and, when he was well, he was a better man. He gave gladly to the poor, and, the more he gave, the more he had to give.

The Stubbornest Man
in Maine

THERE lived a rich man near Booth Bay in Maine who was the stubbornest man in all the state. You could move his stubbornness no more than you could move a hundred-year-old needly pine.

His name was Bill Greenleaf, and when he made up his mind about something in his home neither wife nor child, neither kith nor kin, could out-argue him. He was stubborn as a mule.

It was just the same when he came to the town meetings. He'd say his say, and no man could make him say different any more than you could make thunder thunder different. Family and friends agreed Bill Greenleaf's pesky stubbornness would only end when he went to the better world, where maybe the angels would teach him a little giving in.

One day Bill Greenleaf called his family around him and told them his time had come. Said he:

"I've called ye t'gether to tell ye I don't fancy bein' buried in thick, black earth. I want to be buried in shiny white sand straight from Davenport Bay. From Davenport Bay and no other place." That was a fine bay quite a distance from Squirrel Island where Bill's house stood.

"It's to be from Davenport Bay, and don't ye forget it," he repeated over and over again.

His wife promised it would be done, and Bill Greenleaf died that very night.

At the first peep of dawn Widow Greenleaf sent a big scow with eight strong men to Davenport Bay to bring back enough fine, shiny white sand to bury her late husband, just as he had asked.

The day was clear, and the wind was right, but the scow was heavy, and it was a long, long way to Davenport Bay.

Spoke Peleg who was at the front oar:

"My arms are achin', an' it's rowin' fer no good reason only to please a rantankerous, stubborn dead fellow who can't be stubborn no more. Sand's sand ef it is from Davenport Bay in Maine or out in Chinee Bay."

Michael, who was holding the oar alongside of him, agreed.

"Yer right, Peleg," he said. "Can't see why we got t' suffer from Bill's stubbornness, now he's good 'n' dead."

Moses, who was behind him, pulled hard on his oar, nodded his head, and added:

"We needn't set nothin' by his mulish talk no more

since he's white and meechin'. He can't order us now tellin' us what he wants an' what he don't."

"Reckon the widder won't know the difference from one kind o' sand t' 'nuther. Maybe she don't care neither," added Reuben.

"Let's get the sand right from that place there," cried Jabez, a tall red-haired fellow, pointing to a little inlet right in front of them.

The others agreed at once.

The words put new strength into the arms of the rowers. The heavy scow swung landward, and soon the flat bottom of the vessel scraped the white sand of the shore.

The men took the shovels with a good will, worked hard, and in quick time the vessel was full of the white sand. Then they turned homeward.

Now, when they had set out in the early morning, the sun was shining to warm lizards and the wind was gentle as a lamb, but no sooner did they begin rowing back than there was a quick turn in the weather. The sun rushed behind black clouds, the winds came wildly from the four sides of the compass, and the bay turned into a churning sea.

Reuben and Peleg, Moses and Jabez, and all the others couldn't figure out how it came about, for there had been no sign or warning of a storm.

Rowing was sure hard. The big, heavy, flat-bottomed scow just wouldn't go at all; it lurched and bobbed like a sailor on a spree. At first the sand in the scow flew about in the faces and eyes of the men. Then waves began pouring in over the sides, and the rain came down from above, making the sand brown and soggy and heavy as lead.

With every minute that passed the storm raged worse and worse. The rain was whipping to beat creation, the wind was screeching like painted Indians on the warpath, and the men in the scow were wet and weary and madder than hornets.

Suddenly they saw through the strimmering rain a big figure flapping ghostly-like. It was swaying with the squalls coming nearer and nearer to the boat. The rowing men turned as white as the foam that topped the waves, stopped dead, and just held onto the sides while the scow lurched and dipped and seesawed like crazy.

The big thing wearing a greatcoat came nearer, with arms and coat flapping wildly in the tempest. Now it was near enough for all to see a stubborn whitish face sticking out from the big white collar. And whose face do you think it was!

Jabez roared louder than the racing wind:

"It's old Bill Greenleaf come back!"

He could say no more, for his mouth and throat were so dry that all the water in the bay and all the rain from the sky couldn't take away the dryness. The other men felt no better; they were too scared to say a word.

But Bill Greenleaf, swaying and lurching in the rain, wasn't scared and had plenty to say:

"Aye, ye guessed right, ye crooked-mouthed. humpbacked hypocrites! Ye lyin', blasted good-for-nothin's! Tryin' t' cheat me jest 'cause ye think I'm dead an' gone. I'm dead, certain sure, but I feel t' rejoice, ye untrustful Ananiases, that I ain't gone yet. An' while I'm here-abouts ye ain't goin' t' do things contrary t' the way I want it."

His voice was so big now it filled the whole bay and drowned out the noise of the wind.

"I said, I want t' be buried in white Davenport sand, an' in white Davenport sand I'm goin' t' be buried. Ye were sent t' get sand from Davenport Bay, and yer tryin' t' cheat. Ye didn't suspect I'd be around, but I ain't departed yet, an' I'm goin' t' have things jest the way I want 'em."

He flapped his arms crowlike and bellowed like thunder:

"Take warnin', ye sons o' cheatin' haddocks touched by the Devil's finger! Dump that mess o' mud-sand in the bay quick an' row down Davenport Bay an' get a scowful o' Davenport Bay sand jest as I stipulated. In Davenport Bay sand I'm goin' t' be buried an' no other, mind. An' don't take no year o' Sundays but do it quick, or I'll send ye down so deep in the bay, ye'll drown for sure comin' up."

There was a fast streak of lightning in the sky right then, and just as fast were Jabez, Peleg, Moses, Reuben, and the others dumping shovelfuls of sand into the bay. It wasn't sweet work, for the sand was heavy as rocks, but the men never noticed it.

Old Bill Greenleaf, swaying in the wind, looked on and never said another word.

Funny thing, the less sand there was in the scow, the quieter the wind was over the water and . . . the thinner Bill Greenleaf became.

When the scow was empty and no speck of sand left in it, Bill Greenleaf was gone—and so was the storm.

The men in the scow never said a word. Maybe it was because they were tired, or maybe they thought doing was better than talking. They rowed with all their might to Davenport Bay and loaded the sand fast as a barn a-burning. They rowed back just as fast, loaded the sand in carts, and brought it to God's acre for to bury Bill Greenleaf in it.

That's why people still say Bill Greenleaf is the stubbornest man in all of Maine. For in no other state did anyone ever hear of a man who was as stubborn when he was dead as when he was alive.

The Corsair of Spouting Horn

ON the blue dancing sea in the warm West Indies lay a fine sailing ship. It was the "Quedah Merchant," and from its mast flew the black flag, for it belonged to Captain Kidd the pirate.

Alongside the big ship rocked a slender corsair, and men with grim scarred faces and torn clothes brought from the big ship to the smaller one chests full of gold, silver, gleaming jewels, and shiny cloth.

Two men stood along the rail watching the men at work and talking. They were Captain Kidd and his young lieutenant, Dick Jones. Said Captain Kidd:

"Dick, we couldn't ha' wished for a richer prize nor one less trouble to take."

"Aye, sir," young Dick replied, " 'twas simple indeed, Captain. Luck's ever on your side."

"Would it were so—always. . . ." He was silent for a time, thinking of his wife and child. For pirates often love wife and child full as much as others do. Then he spoke again:

"You're taking Ruth, your young wife, along on the voyage up home."

"That I am, sir."

"You know 'tis said it's ill luck to have a woman aboard."

"Ruth has brought me much luck and joy. Besides, I am a better sailor when she is near me." And Dick laughed so that his teeth gleamed in the sun and his eyes sparkled bright.

"Still I say, Dick, it'd be better if you left her with us here in the warm Indies. Up in Maine it's cold and dangerous, and you'll come back quicker for knowing she is here waiting."

"I'll come back quicker with her, Captain Kidd. My heart is wherever she is; to leave her here is to leave my heart as well. And a sailor without a heart is like a ship without a rudder."

The captain shook his head but said no more about it. Instead he spoke of the place where the treasure was to be hid.

The craft was ready. The men bade each other good-by and good journey, and the corsair went off skimming like a bird on wings.

It was a swift voyage and a safe one. Day upon day of sunshine and favorable winds, and—no sail in sight. This was what Dick wanted most, for he would rather not meet merchantman or warship while he had the great treasure in the hold.

The boat flew fast, the sun shone warm, and the men,

used to fierce battle and plunder, were peaceful and contented. Most contented of all were Dick and Ruth of the dark brown eyes and the gleaming brown hair. For once she knew neither fear nor worry for the man she loved. She wished they'd never go back to the "Quedah Merchant" and Captain Kidd, but she did not say it loud. When they were alone she pleaded with Dick to give up his pirate life for one of peace and ease. He promised, for he loved her dearly.

So they reached the waters near New England and came up the rocky coast of Maine. There they turned the bow toward Mount Desert, where the treasure was to be hid in a cave not far from the sea.

The sun set red with streaks of clouds, and in the morning the fog was thick as a gray blanket. It was the northern fog that loves the coast of Maine even more than the far North—to this very day.

Lieutenant Dick drew his sails close and went cautiously along the coast. He knew full well how treacherous the shore was and tried to find a safe landing place. Never did he leave the wet deck, and Ruth was always by his side.

So a day and night passed in solid fog, and the next day was no better. In the late forenoon the thick gray blanket thinned a little, and it seemed to Dick he would now find his way to safety—when all of a sudden he sighted a strong corvette flying a British flag. Captain and crew looked on the vessel none too pleased, and the captain and crew of the corvette looked on the corsair with suspicion.

Suddenly there was a rounding ball of smoke on the corvette and a warning shot flew across the bow right near where Dick and Ruth were standing. 'Twas a shot warning them either to come alongside the warship or let the British sailors come aboard the corsair. Whichever they did, it meant imprisonment and maybe death for Dick and his pirate crew.

But Dick wasn't the kind to be frightened easily; his orders were sharp and quick.

"Head for the coast, never mind rocks and danger. An inlet that'll shield us must be found."

His words were obeyed, and the nose of the boat turned toward the bleak, jagged rocks that looked threatening and forbidding. Dick and every man on boat watched close, and Ruth stood by in her big dark cloak, as fearless as the rest.

The full wind blew fierce, and the boat raced swiftly to the broken cliffs. Luck smiled at Dick and Ruth, and their eyes shone bright. There, to the right, was a narrow channel, enough to let the little corsair pass to safety, but not wide enough for the corvette to enter.

The captain of the corvette saw it, too, and let loose broadside after broadside, but all he hit was the white boiling water and the rocky coast.

Now the corsair was nearing the opening beyond which no ship could harm her while shots were falling right and left. There was the path and . . . freedom—

when a shot hit the helmsman at the wheel and set him flying along the deck. It cut the halyard stays and brought the mainsail crashing down.

The boat turned and twisted like a wounded thing. The wild sea and fierce wind beat it all around—tearing, pulling toward the threatening coast.

Dick flung himself on the wheel, but it was of little use; the boat could not be led to safety now. The raging wind raised it high like a stick of wood and flung it fiercely against the sharp black edges of the rocks, Spouting Horn the place is called. Then the boat crashed fiercely into the whipping white waters. Masts, planks flew apart, men disappeared. All save one, Ruth, her cloak torn from her, her brown hair wet and straggly yet flying in the wind. She was kneeling on the deck, praying.

Sea and wind seemed angrier at the sight. Wild waves dashed up, howling blasts rushed on, once again they lifted the boat and dashed it against the rocks. It fell apart, and the churning sea sucked it down—forever! No, not forever.

For on gray wild days, when the North fogs come visiting Spouting Horn, there, in the twilight hour, you will see a shadowy little corsair, slender as a young girl, sailing toward the rocky coast.

On the deck stand a ghostly young officer and a young girl in a long cloak with streaming hair, both looking eagerly toward the coast, seeking a haven of peace. . . .

The Smart Woman of Kennebunkport

ONCE upon a time,
When maple syrup dripped from the eaves,
And salt grew on lettuce leaves,
there lived a smart old widow woman in Kennebunkport who had an answer for every quip, a turn for
every trick, and wasn't afraid of anything. Her name
was Widow Watson, and most of the smart fellows of
the town didn't like her and said she was just nasty-nice.
They were forever scheming how to take the wind out
of her sails.

One day, three of these smart fellows, Ezra, Ira, and
Elias, thought up a scheme to scare the good old lady,
body and boots.

On a dark night when Widow Watson was coming
home from a little talk with the neighbors on the next
farm she had to go through a thick pine woods.

A sliver of a moon shone on high, and there was a
sweet smell of green needles and wild flowers.

But all of a sudden there was a yowling and yelping

and screaming and screeching from all around that would frighten cats in the dark.

The good widow stopped short in surprise and listened; then she shrugged her shoulders, walked her way, and said:

"Dunno what the rumpus's about, but it is no concern o' mine."

Now you sure must know it was Ezra, Ira, and Elias who made all the noise to frighten the good woman. They were much surprised, as you can guess, when they saw her walking along, not frightened at all. They didn't know yet they had brought their pigs to the wrong market.

They kept on hollering, booming, and squealing like Ding-balls and Will-am-alones, the strange beasts in the lumberland of Maine. But old Widow Watson, she just kept walking without fear or fancy, minding her own affairs. That was a bit too much for Ezra, Ira, and Elias.

So Ezra leaped out, his face all black, cow horns on his head, and a dark cloak around him, a-dancing and cavorting before her.

Widow Watson looked at him and just kept on walking.

"It's the Devil!" screamed Ira.

"It's the Devil!" screeched Elias. "Ain't ye afeared, Widow Watson?"

Then the old lady opened her mouth and said:

"Howdy-due, ye pack o' nimshis! Them that serves the Devil by day are afeared o' him at night. I don't

serve him by day, so I ain't afeared o' him at night."
And she kept on her way, for she guessed bright and
quick the game of these three.

Well, that didn't take the wind out o' Ezra, Ira, and
Elias. They went home racking their heads like a po-
tato field, figuring how they'd teach that woman a lesson she'd never forget.

One day not long after, there came a peddler to town
with tins and pans, needles and notions, and also a monkey a sailor coming from Africa had given him.

No monkey had even been seen in Kennebunkport,
so Ezra, Ira, and Elias bought that monkey just to scare
Widow Watson good and proper.

One day when she was away, they put the little animal inside her clapboard cottage and hid behind the
window to watch the fun when she'd see the creature
for the first time.

Soon she came home and went into the kitchen, and
there on the wooden beam sat the hairy little beast with
the long arms, long legs, a long tail, twitching its little
eyes. Well, Widow Watson just looked and looked,
eyes wide open, trying to figure out whether it was beast,
devil, or maybe her husband, who had led an evil life,
come back.

Suddenly the animal began chattering. Then it ran
along the beam and swung itself down on one foot, reach-
ing down into the basket of eggs. The monkey picked
up one of them and threw it at her. Then it picked up
another and another, throwing them at her from all

sides. That raised Widow Watson's dander, high as a church steeple.

"I thought ye were the Devil in disguise," she screamed. "Now I know ye're my late husband. Ye never wanted me to eat eggs 'cause ye wanted 'em fer yerself; now ye're breakin' 'em jest to spite me. But ye got the wrong pig by the ear. Get out o' here an' go back where ye came from."

With that she picked up the brush broom and began chasing the animal all over the place. The door flung open, and the monkey ran out as quick as its long legs would carry it. Widow Watson ran out too, and there she saw Ezra, Ira, and Elias holding their sides with laughter.

"So it's ye three actin' up again," she screamed. "It's about time ye know ye can't knock my house down. Ye need more strings to yer bow than ye got to get the best o' Widow Watson."

Well, Ezra, Ira, and Elias knew they had enough and it was no use trying a third time, nor any other time, either. Instead they became good friends with Widow Watson, ever laughing at her smart quips and clever tricks. Which was much better, wasn't it?

Tall Barney Beal

IN granite Maine, the weather is fickle as women and weird as windigos, and it's worst of all on Fridays when witches are queens. But the grass grows green, the trees grow tall, and the sea is rich—and no Maine Man would change the weather with that of any other state.

Some sons of Maine, too, are just like Maine weather, and such was Tall Barney Beal, the finest fisherman up and down the rocky coast. Barney Beal said he was Paul Bunyan's first cousin, for he was six foot seven tall in his red woolen socks, could fish better and fight harder than a full man-o'-war's crew on a spree. From Rowdy Head to Cape Elizabeth and thereabouts, people called him the Cock o' the Walk, and the name fitted him mighty good.

One Friday morn he rose betimes, and his nose was itching two fathoms deep. That was a bad sign, but Tall Barney Beal, that big pine-man, never worried his head about bad signs. He jumped from his bunk, looked out of the window, and saw a fog thick enough to hold nails for hanging boots.

"Fog's thick, but that ain't goin' to stop me from goin' fishin' for smelts. The weather o' Maine kin be fickle's women and weird's windigos, but no kind o' weather kin beat Tall Barney Beal," he grumbled to himself. Then he made a fire to fry him some dough-nuts, and while waiting for the doughnuts to brown he sat in the rocker, a-rocking. His long, long arms reached down to the wooden planks of the floor and helped in the rocking.

Now you must know Tall Barney Beal was a-frying Coffin doughnuts, the kind that can be found only in the State of Maine. These are doughnuts that turn over by themselves so they brown even on both sides. When they are brown on both sides they leap clean from the fat into your mouth. But this Friday morning witches were queens and the weather was fickle. The doughnuts were contrary and jumped onto the broad floor beams instead of into Tall Barney's broad mouth. It raised his dander high, and he came up a-scudding from the rocker and bellowed:

"A man like me kin fish jest's good eatin' reg'lar doughnuts 'stead o' Coffin doughnuts."

He put on his gray butcher's coat, the kind he always wore, and went out. The fog was gone, and there was lightning and thunder in the sky.

"See we got a Maine weather day, fickle's women and weird's windigos, but that ain't a-stoppin' me from fishin'," he said to himself.

He walked along the cobbled street and saw Josiah

Bangs, the little ship-carpenter man with a red beard under his chin. The mite of a fellow was leaning against his little white clapboard house.

"Where away, Tall Barney, this wet Friday mornin'?"

"Goin' fishin'."

"Friday's a bad day for fishin', the weather's kitt'nish. Think snow's comin'."

"Yer talkin' vinegar. Reckon I kin make my own fishin' weather and lick Friday bad luck fifty fathom deep."

"Think ye're smart, Big Barney, but some day somethin'll happen an' ye'll be tame's a dead whale."

Tall Barney had a temper, and Josiah's words made him mad as a merman chasing seagulls. He bellowed:

"I'll show ye how tame I kin be." He put his shoulders against Josiah Bang's little clapboard house and pushed it clear five or maybe seven feet out of the way. Then he went off blowing and snorting.

The thunder was gone, and snow and rain were playing leapfrog all around.

Tall Barney took out his boat while a stiff sou'wester was driving hard and rain thick as waterfalls was coming down to help fill the ocean. He fished all over the sea, the boat rolling and veering, scudding and spinning, dancing and dipping like witches going to the Sabbath. But with all the trying no fish would come.

Suddenly the clouds broke, and Tall Barney Beal saw alongside his craft a boatful of British sailors straight from a man-o'-war. They boarded his sloop and told him he was in British waters and he'd better make himself scarce as a mermaid.

Do you think Tall Barney was scared? Not he! He just took the Britishers by their shoulders, knocked their heads together, and when they fell down, Kerplunk! he took their long guns in his big hands and broke each of them in half. This scared the sailors white.

Some more redcoats came on the sloop to hold up their courage. Then Tall Barney spread his big legs wide apart and began rocking the boat from side to side, from side to side, quicker and quicker all the time. Soon the sides were close to the water. Deeper and deeper went the craft, and the Britishers fell into the sea, legs high in the air, till not a one was left and Tall Barney turned the nose of his craft homeward.

The wind blew fresh, the sky was clear, the sun shone golden, and Tall Barney felt gay as a gull.

He walked along the cobblestone street whistling an old ditty, "Blow the Man Down." There stood Josiah Banks near his clapboard house five feet or maybe seven out on the road.

"Any luck?" he cried.

"No luck at all, Josiah. Should've listened to yer words this mornin'. I'll know better the next time. Now I'll push yer house back to where it stood."

He spread his legs wide and put his shoulders to the house and pushed with might and main. Soon the house stood in the same spot where it had been built.

Home Barney went roaring "Blow the Man Down," cooked him a pot of beans, smelts, and pork chops, and no king ever had a better meal. When he sat on his rocker, rocking back and forth, his long arms hanging down to the wide wooden floor, he promised himself he'd never go fishin' again on Friday's morn when witches are queens and Maine weather is fickle as women and weird as windigos.

WHITE

MOUNTAINS

Lincoln °

The Granite State
of
NEW HAMPSHIRE

Mont Vernon °

Portsmouth
Exeter °

Cinderella of New Hampshire

747886

ONCE upon a time, and not so long ago, there lived way up in New Hampshire colony, in Portsmouth town, a little girl by the name of Martha Hilton. She was very poor, and from early morning till late at night she worked at the Inn of the Earl of Halifax that was owned by Mistress Stavers.

All day long she was busy washing dishes, cleaning, and carrying heavy pails of water. She wore rags for clothes and had no shoes on her feet. Often, she did not even have time to comb her hair, but with all that she was the prettiest girl in the town, and she was ever happy. On her rosy, red lips and in her dancing brown eyes there was ever a smile, and all were kind to her except her mistress. She was forever scolding her, morning, noon, and night. But she scolded her most of all when Martha, her eyes laughing, would say:

"You may scold me all you want, Mistress Stavers; you may give me rags for clothes and stale bread for food, but some day I'll ride in a carriage of gold with fine, white, prancing steeds."

37

This would make Mistress Stavers scold her more, and sometimes even beat her.

One fine day when the wind sang in the corn there was grand company in the Inn of Mistress Stavers. All the men of the town were there making merry. But poor little Martha had to work harder than ever fetching wood and water.

Now all the boys and girls of Portsmouth liked Martha and always helped her when they could. On that day John, the blacksmith's son, carried the heavy pails of water from the spring for her. Mistress Stavers happened to come out of the Inn and saw it. Her fat face grew purple with anger, and her big body shook like a tree in a hurricane.

"You lazy good-for-nothing," she screamed. "I suppose you think you're too fine for work, letting others do it for you. Eating my bread and sleeping under my roof is well enough, but as for helping me, you must get the boys of the street for it. From now on you can sleep with the pigs and not in my good house."

"I work hard and I try my best, Mistress Stavers, yet no matter how hard I work and try you are forever scolding me." For a minute Martha looked sad, then a smile brightened her face and she said, "There's no harm sleeping with pigs, but some day I'll ride in a gilded carriage with fine, white, prancing steeds."

That made Mistress Stavers angrier, and she screamed and scolded even louder, calling Martha all kinds of names.

It so happened that at the very time the Governor of New Hampshire came walking by. He truly looked like a Governor, in his scarlet coat with silver buttons, and red shoes with silver buckles.

He stopped short when he heard Dame Stavers screaming and scolding pretty Martha.

"Why all the noise and why all the screaming, Mistress Stavers?" asked the Governor.

The mistress of the Earl of Halifax Inn, not in the least ashamed, began telling the Governor all about Martha. She was lazy, she was always letting others work for her, she was forever telling she'd ride in a carriage of gold with prancing white steeds! And wasn't this enough to make any decent body mad?

"Is this true, pretty little Martha?" asked the Governor.

"Not all true," Martha replied quickly. "I'm not lazy, and I work hard from morning to night, even though my friends help me a little sometimes. What if I do say that some day I'll ride in a gilded carriage with fine, white, prancing steeds? Any maid has a right to say that."

"Aye, that's true indeed," said the Governor. "Zounds! you're pretty enough to fit in a carriage of gold with white prancing steeds." Then turning to Dame Stavers he added:

"If she's such a poor kitchen maid, why do you keep her?"

"I'm sending her flying right this minute. Never

again can she come into my house and eat at my table."

"That being the case, I'll take her to my own mansion, where I have need of a maid right now."

"You're getting a poor bargain, Governor," said Dame Stavers. "Go pack your rags at once, you good-for-nothing slut, and don't ever set foot in my house again." Then she went into the Inn all puffed up with anger.

Martha did not need any coaxing. She too went into the Inn. Before you could count five she was out again with a small bundle under her arm, following the royal Governor to his mansion.

How different life was there! She had nice clothes, and a fine bed to sleep in, and she did her work so well that, instead of scolding, everyone was kind to her.

So the time went by very happily for Martha, who was growing prettier every month and every year.

She was so pretty that she became known in all the colony of New Hampshire for her beauty.

Many suitors came to woo her. There were sailors, soldiers, and merchantment, but to all she had only one answer:

"I've time enough for marrying. And when I do," this she added laughing, "I'll ride in a gilded coach with fine, white, prancing steeds."

Everybody in town heard her say it, and Governor Wentworth, too. He was a widower and missed a wife in his house.

The more he looked at Martha and saw how beautiful

she was, the more he thought she'd fit perfectly as a mistress in his rich mansion. What if she was a kitchen maid? A prince married Cinderella!

One day when she was all alone in the kitchen, standing over the hot pots, her face rosy as a September apple, he went in and said:

"Pretty Martha, I've heard you often say you'd ride in a gilded coach with fine, white, prancing steeds."

"That I have, Your Excellency," she replied, blushing prettily and making a curtsey as fine as any lady's, "but I meant it only as a jest."

"Often a jest is seed to the truth. Won't you be my wedded wife? Then you'll surely ride in a gilded coach drawn by fine, prancing steeds. You're pretty and kind and smart and good enough to grace any Governor's mansion!"

Martha needed no coaxing and quickly said the word.

"Three weeks hence is my birthday. That'll be our wedding day, but don't breathe a word to any soul in town," said the Governor. "I'll get you the most beautiful wedding gown in all of great America; then Rector Brown'll marry us."

The Governor invited all the officers and all the councilors as well as Rector Brown to celebrate his birthday. Meanwhile, Martha got her jewels and a wedding gown of silver and gilded lace.

The day of the Governor's birthday came, and the grand company arrived, dressed in their finest and best. Martha, too, was dressed in her finest and best. In her silver and lace wedding gown and silver slippers she was more beautiful than words can tell or pen can write. And who do you think was helping to dress her? Why, none other than Mistress Stavers!

Forgotten were the scoldings of former days. Mistress Stavers even said the scoldings had been a fine thing for, because of them, Martha had come to the Governor's mansion. And, since Martha was the happiest girl in all the colony, she bore no grudge to any soul nor to Mistress Stavers.

In the chamber of state with silver candlesticks and carved chairs sat the Governor and the great men of the colony, feasting and making merry. Up rose one of the councilors and, lifting his glass high, toasted the Governor on his birthday, wishing him many, many more of them.

The Governor stood up and thanked him. Then he said, "This is a happy day indeed. It's my birthday, and it shall likewise be my wedding day."

"Who's the lady?" they cried one and all. "Who's the lucky one?"

"Why, none other than Martha Hilton, my kitchen maid, more lovely than Cinderella ever was. She'll be the royal Governor's wife. Rector Brown'll marry us right now."

You should have seen the faces of the noble company and heard their words!

"What? A kitchen maid wife to our Governor? We'll have to call her M'Lady! Why, such things aren't heard

of save in fairy tales, and those are only in books."
Even Rector Brown grumbled and said he'd never marry
them.

"Silence," cried the Governor. "You, Rector Brown,
'll marry us right now. I command it!"

Out he went and soon came in with Martha, who
was a vision of loveliness.

When the noble company saw how beautiful the
bride was, they forgave Governor Wentworth quickly
enough. Rector Brown married them, and they were
very happy.

And when Martha rode through Portsmouth town,
she rode in a gilded carriage with fine, white, prancing
steeds as she had said she would when she was a kitchen
maid.

Three Times and Out

THREE times the Devil tried to get the good people of New Hampshire in his clutches, three times he failed, and he didn't try much thenafter for he knew it was no use.

This is how he tried the first time. One day he looked up and down New England, and his evil eye fell on the beautiful White Mountains of New Hampshire.

"Oh!" he cried. "No witch was ever hunted there as in Salem or Boston town, and I can remedy that. Soon I'll have them dancing around the gallows."

He took a great leap and landed in the heart of the beautiful clear White Mountains, looked around, and saw his chance.

In a fine house he noticed old General Jonathan sitting afore his fire drinking hot cider with spices from both the Indies. The general was figuring hard how he could make more money than anyone in all the state—maybe in all the world.

"Ha!" he roared. "I'd even sell my soul to the Devil if I could get all the money I want."

"Suits me fine," said the Evil One, leaping out of the chimney right before the general, while fiery sparks flew from his velvet suit and the horns on his head.

"I'll give you all the gold you want; just sign this parchment scroll with a drop of blood from your finger."

"How do I know I can trust you?" said the general.

"That's simple," cried the Evil One, running his long nails through his black peruke and around the little horns. At once gold pieces flew all over the room.

Before they even were on the ground the general leaped over them. But no sooner did he touch them than he let out a fierce yell. The gold was burning hot.

"Not so fast, my good friend, not so fast. You must wait for my permission. Now I give it to you. Take the money."

The general didn't need another word. He raked up all the coins on that wooden floor and put them quickly into the pocket of his greatcoat.

"That's my proof, General," said the Evil One. "Here's my bargain. On the first day of every month hang your boots in the chimney and I'll fill 'em with gold . . . for your soul—when the proper time comes. Here, sign the parchment."

"I'll sign," said the general slowly ". . . but the bargain only holds as long as I get my boots full of money."

"Come, sign," Old Scratch said impatiently. "I must return to Salem."

General Jonathan pricked his finger and signed. Then the Devil, putting his black mantle around him, vanished through the chimney.

After that, gold flowed regularly into the general's boots so that he truly became the richest man in all New England. But no matter how much gold he had he still wanted more. One fine day he hit on a pretty scheme. He chuckled and laughed and slapped his thighs and felt better than he ever had before.

The next time the Evil One stood on the chimney pouring the gold down into the boots he noticed there was no end to the pouring. No matter how much he poured down, the boots would not fill.

"Now, that's a strange thing," he said, scratching his horns. "I must look into this." So he climbed down and saw . . . there were no soles in the boots! The wily old general had cut off the soles so that the gold never stopped flowing through the boots.

The Devil was hog-wild, and he let out a yell that could be heard clear across the land.

"I'll teach that thief a lesson," he screamed and leaped up the chimney while fiery sparks flew from his hands in all directions. Some fell on the roof shingles. The house caught fire and burned so fiercely that all the gold melted together.

"You'll remember this, you cheating knave!" screamed the Evil One. "It's the last gold you'll ever see."

"Then you can't have my soul," cried the general. "And the gold is mine, for molten gold is still good gold."

"I'll get your soul yet, never fear. As for the gold, we'll see about that!" And the Devil flew off in a roaring rage.

He flew up and down the state looking for a second chance to start his evil witch-hunting ways in New Hampshire.

So he came to Mont Vernon. There people were ever eating fat, brown beans. They loved eating beans from their bean-pots more than anything else in the world, just as General Jonathan loved gold more than anything else.

"Oh ho! I'll catch these fellows with their love of eating more than they need. I'll promise them a bean-pot that will always be full of beans cooked with everything that's fine for cooking in New England—in return for their souls. They are simple people and won't cheat like that thieving general."

First he looked around for the biggest bean-pot there was and found one in a gorge in the hills where there was a hole in the stone big enough to hold barrels full. Then he came to the elders of the town and told them they could have all the beans in the world without sowing, reaping, or cooking. They would always find them freshly cooked in a big stone pot—if only they would sell to him their souls, and those of the townspeople they represented, by signing a little piece of parchment.

The elders loved beans, but they didn't trust the Devil and said so.

"I'll give you good proof first," replied the Evil One. "Come Saturday night, which is bean night, to the mountain gorge. There you'll see the stone bean-pot that will always be full of beans on Saturday night if you just sign your souls away and those of your towns-men for whom you can speak."

"We'll come and bring the people," the head man said. "Only make certain no one recognizes you. For they might not want to enter into a bargain with you."

"Oh! I'll take care of that. You just come ready to sign."

Young and old, big and little, went on the set night to the gorge. The Devil came in a long velvet cloak to hide his cloven foot, and a high peaked cap to hide his black horns. He seated everyone politely around the big boiling stone pot which was covered all around with sizzling fiery coals and from which came the sweetest brown smell in all the world of baking beans. Brown beans with fat salt pork, maple syrup, dry mustard, bay leaves, and little onions sitting on the top like bonnets. It made every good townsman's mouth water enough to make a good-sized river.

So they sat around smacking their lips while the Devil gave each a wooden plate and a wooden spoon. Then, taking a great big wooden ladle in his hand, he walked up to the seething pot to get the beans.

Now, to make sure the beans would be well cooked, the Evil One had made the fire so fierce that stones and rocks all around began to melt. He never thought of this, so anxious was he to get all these New England souls in one haul. No sooner did he get near the pot than his right foot sank deep, deep into the fiery molten stone! The imprint on the rock can be seen there to this very day; it is seven feet long. The Devil let out a piercing yell that could be heard from one end of the land to the other and leaped high in the air. His peaked cap flew off, his cloak fell down, and the good Mont Vernon people saw, by the glare of the fire, the horns, the long tail, and the cloven foot. They knew at once it was the Devil in person tempting them, so they rose one and all and fled repenting their silly gluttony.

From that day on they never wanted more beans than they could eat.

The Devil, seeing how he had lost out the second time, ran into the gorge to nurse his burning foot. But he wasn't yet ready to give up wanting White Mountain people in his evil fold. The Devil does not give up easily.

"I'll try just once more—a third time," he said. "This time I must succeed. If I don't . . . I'll not waste my time here any longer."

His foot healed, and he began looking up and down and all around until he spied Mistress Bailey, who was jealous of everything walking or creeping.

"Oh ho!" he cried. "Here is just the right woman for me. Jealousy is as bad as gluttony. She'll make a fine witch!"

Mistress Bailey was leaning against the barn door figuring how she could harm Mistress Simon, who owned a finer house and fatter cattle than she herself had. Suddenly there was lightning, thunder, a great gust of wind, and then right next to Mistress Bailey stood a tall gentleman dressed in black velvet, a long cloak around him and a peaked cap on his head. He helped her stand up against the wind and they spoke of this and that. Very soon the Evil One promised Mistress Bailey that Mistress Simon would be plagued as no woman was ever plagued in all New England, if only Mistress Bailey would say she'd join the black gentleman seven days from that day, which was a Wednesday. Then she'd go where she could do all the evil she wanted, to anyone she did not like. The bargain was sealed with a drop of blood from her little finger.

Mistress Bailey could hardly walk from excitement, and the black-coated gentleman helped her into the chamber, where she fell asleep at once.

The next morning she thought of what she had done and was very unhappy, for after all Mistress Simon was not so bad. True, she had some faults and had many things Mistress Bailey wanted, but maybe Mistress Bailey had things Mistress Simon wanted. She was afeared of going with the tall man. Her own farm was so nice! and Heaven so bright!

She told her tale to a neighbor who told it to a neighbor who told it to a neighbor, and before the evening was over the good minister of the town knew it. He spoke to Mistress Bailey and avowed he would save her.

Wednesday came, and all the people gathered; so did the town's minister and twelve ministers from neighboring towns as well.

At the set hour the ministers formed a circle around Mistress Bailey, who was on her knees. Around the ministers gathered the deacons, around them a circle of elders, and around them all the people of the town.

They all sang and prayed and shouted for the Lord to keep the black Tempter away from Mistress Bailey.

The Devil came, and though he tried more than a hundred times he couldn't get through that wall of prayers, singing, and shouting of ministers, deacons, and people.

It made the Evil One angrier than General Jonathan's cutting the soles of his boots, and the burning of his own feet in the fiery stones.

"Three times I've tried," he cried, "and I'm tired of trying. I'll go where it's easier catching souls than in New Hampshire."

So it happened that there was no witch-hunting in the beautiful White Mountain State of New Hampshire.

The Fairies in
the White Mountains

WHEN the Indians roamed the land far and wide, there were fairies up in the White Mountains of New Hampshire. During the day they hid in the long ferns and soft moss, and at night they played by the light of the moon and danced to the song of the whippoorwills just like fairies in any other land. For food they ate fairy bread, and often they fed this to Indian children, who would then turn into fairies and remain with them forever. But the fairies never gave it to the children of the white settlers, though they wanted to. For they had no power over white children.

One day Sarah, a little white girl who lived in Warren near Hurricane Brook, where these fairies were, was lost in the woods. Her father and mother had gone visiting, and Sarah wanted to go along. Instead of listening to her mother and staying behind to play with the other children, she followed them and soon could not find her way amongst the hemlocks and the pines.

Sarah was neither afraid nor dismayed, but she was hungry. So she sat down, tired, against a giant pine tree and soon fell asleep. She slept for many hours until the silver moonlight awoke her. She was very hungry and began to cry, but not for long. Soon the little fairies who were near by heard her. First they were afraid to come near, but, when they saw that she was no different from Indian girls, they came up and gave her wild strawberries and fairy bread to eat. Sarah ate and ate until she wasn't hungry any more. Then she joined in the fairies' games and dancing. When she grew tired they called the biggest bear in the woods and told him he'd have to be Sarah's soft, warm bed. The bear lay down under the tree, and since Sarah loved animals, and thought the bear was a big black dog, she lay down on his warm fur and went to sleep as happily as if she were in her own home.

But in her home there was no happiness, the very opposite. Her folks were worried to distraction. Her mother cried, and her parents' friends and neighbors were searching day and night, seeking the little lost girl.

So days passed, with Sarah living amongst the fragrant blossoms and pines that smelled sweet as a garden, while all the settlers were searching wood and dale for her, with sorrow in their hearts.

But soon little Sarah grew homesick. She wanted to be with her mother and father, her sisters and brothers and friends. She told it to the fairies, whispered it to the bear, and begged all the time to be sent home, promising to come back.

She begged so long and so hard that the fairies promised to send her home if she would but stay another day.

That night the fairies sent a dream three times over again to a man who loved children, showing him the giant pine tree where Sarah was.

The next morning he came to Warren town and told of the dream he had had three times in one night. Sarah's father and friends listened to him and then went straightway through the woods along the path where the bear had walked on the moss and leaves. Soon they came to the giant pine tree the man had seen in his dreams, and there they found Sarah waiting for them.

You can just imagine how happy everyone was. They hugged and kissed her and made her tell a hundred times over how she was fed and how she slept with the big black "dog."

Some believed and some did not, but you and I do, for how could a little girl live so many days in the woods all alone without parents and friends?

But all those who believed and those who did not were happy to have found Sarah. They made a great celebration and ate beans cooked with salt pork and sweet molasses, blew tin horns, shouted and hurrahed, just as they did on the happy Fourth of July.

Holding the Bag

IN Exeter, in the rolling hills where the salty ocean smells come on windy days, most men fought hard for their freedom, many learned good learning, and some acted silly. That's the way of the world, and thereby hangs a tale about Rainsy Rogers.

Rainsford Rogers, slick as a soaped eel, went up and down the New England states playing dishonest with young and old. It made him rich, but only because people were greedy, and when people are greedy they are unwise and foolish. So he came to Exeter, where he met Squire Jeremiah and other men of note and gave them a big string of talk about a great treasure hidden by pirates near the town. He was the only one who could find it, for he had the power to raise and lay spirits of the other world, both good and evil. And since Jeremiah, who was a rich man, and his friends, who were rich as well, were greedy, wisdom left them, and they wanted more gold, though they had plenty of it. They listened to Rainsy and believed him.

But there was one friend of Jeremiah, named Jonathan Ladd, who was contented with what he had and saw clearly that Rainsford Rogers was a rogue ready to cheat friend and foe. He told this to Jeremiah a hundred times over, but it did little good. He told him he had the greatest treasure in all the world, for he had a happy home, good children, enough to eat and make merry. It was of no avail. So he was silent, figuring that some men must learn to walk through the forest of life by knocking their heads hard against many trees.

As for Jeremiah and his friends, they went many a night with Rainsy Rogers into the woods with spades and lanterns, digging and digging and digging. Yet with all the digging not a gold piece or silver was ever found.

Then Rainsy Rogers said:

"The ghosts said you must wear ghostly clothes and then they'll lead you to the treasure. Each one must wear a snow-white cap so the spirits'll see you better."

The next time they went a-digging each man wore a snow-white cap on his head. They were a strange sight, these men, with their white caps, digging and digging, sweat running from their brows. Squire Ladd said they were a pack of fools making worse fools of themselves by listening to a swindler. But he was talking to deaf ears; greed had closed them tight.

Night after night they dug and dug, but never a coin was found. One night they were digging in the dismal swamp and all were worn and tired. Suddenly there came out of the dark mist a ghost all covered white. It might have been a man or it might have been a woman, I'll let you guess which. It asked them why they were there.

"We are seeking the pirate's treasure," cried Jeremiah. "Won't you please tell us, Squire Ghost, where it's hidden?"

The ghost spoke, but he mumbled so low no one could understand.

"Speak a mite louder, Squire Ghost," cried one of the diggers. "I'm hard o' hearing."

But the ghost was gone before you could say Jack Robinson, leaving the tired diggers deep in the mud and swamp and no nearer to the gold they sought and did not need.

The next day they saw Rainsy Rogers. When they told him of the ghost, he said:

"That ghost came to me, too, an' told me a way to surely find the treasure without more delay. He said I must get at once a divining rod made of precious things found only in Philadelphia. It will cost many hundred dollars, but the rod will repay us many times the sum."

When Squire Ladd heard this, he cried that Jeremiah and the others were the greatest fools that could be found in all New England. "That cheat'll keep the money and you'll hold the bag," he said.

But all his warning did little good. Jeremiah and his friends raised the sum and brought it in a strong carpet

bag to Rainsy Rogers in the dark of night. He ordered
them to go into the thick swamp near by with spades
and shovels and wait for him, while he was flying on his
magic horse to Philadelphia. He'd return before the
cock's crow with the magic rod.

The silly men of Exeter waited till the cold dawn
came. Then they went home silently, each thinking his
own thoughts.

When the sun was up Squire Ladd came for Jeremiah
to go to Portsmouth to buy some sheep. Squire Ladd
asked about the treasure hunt, but Jeremiah never said
a word. So they went into the stable, and when they
came in they saw that . . . Squire Jeremiah's finest
horse and best saddle were gone.

"Where's my horse?" stormed Jeremiah.

"Master," said the stable boy, "Squire Rainsford Rogers came last night carrying a leather bag an' said you'd
tol' him to get the horse for you. Then he emptied what
was in the carpet bag into his leather bag, tied it on the
saddle, and went off. He left the empty carpet bag. It's
there hangin' on a peg."

You should have seen Jeremiah's face.

"Friend," said Squire Ladd, "I told you you'd remain
just holding the empty bag. The bird with the gold has
flown. You'll never see his face here again."

And never was his face seen in Exeter town again.
'Twas a good thing it wasn't. The scales of greed fell
from the eyes of Jeremiah and his friends; they saw they

needed no pirates' gold to make them rich when they had their good farms and happy families. No one ever spoke of Rainsy Rogers, but sometimes people made fun of Jeremiah and his friends about white caps and holding the bag!

The Giant of the Hills

HIGH in a mountain notch there lived three brothers bigger than any men thereabout. The biggest of the three was Ethan Allen Crawford, and people called him the Giant of the Hills.

He was big as Paul Bunyan and just as strong. His voice could be heard over seven miles going strong, and he had strength to carry a giant bear fifty miles or more without breathing hard.

What's more he was smart as a weasel, kind as a mother, and just as a judge. So every man and every animal loved that big Ethan Allen.

One sharp winter night, when the moon and stars shone clear as ice, Ethan was suddenly awakened from his deep slumber by the noise of howling wolves, bleating lambs, neighing horses, and bellowing cows.

He opened his eyes, stuck out his head from under his bear coverlet, and, in a voice that shook the timbers and rocked the walls, he said to Nate, there for a visit and sleeping next to him:

"Nate, wonder what the rumpus's about."

"Wolves," Nate said, shivering.

"We better get up and finish 'em quick," said Ethan. But neither made a move to rise, though the howling and bleating and bellowing grew worse.

"You got no powder in the house, an' we even haven't a good cudgel around. We burned all the wood for fire to keep the cold out. Guess we got to leave the wolves have their way this time."

"There ain't no powder and there ain't no trees in the house, but I still got my voice an' my strong bare fists, an' I'll let no wolves take my beasts away."

"Wouldn't take the chance with a pack of hungry wolves, Eth'. Cheaper to let 'em feed. You better stay under your bearskin, Ethan Allen Crawford. It's cold 'nuf to freeze the tongue in your mouth."

"I'm goin' to save them animals if I got to do it by preachin'."

"Preachin' to people is most o' the time little good, and sure won't be no good at all to wild wolves. I tell ye, stay in here an' fer once let 'em have their fill."

"Not me," roared Ethan, leaping from his bed. Without waiting to put on clothes against the bitter cold, with no weapon in his hand for defense, he ran to the door and unlatched it quick, his dogs close at his heels.

"Stay here. I kin handle a pack o' wolves single-handed," he shouted to the dogs.

There in the cold white moonlight was a sight to frighten any man. Sheep and oxen, cows and horses, made a noise loud as Niagara Falls, while four fierce wolves with gleaming eyes and hanging, slimy tongues howled and snarled, watching for a chance to get one of the animals.

Ethan, standing at the door with his stocking feet and white nightshirt, began roaring with a voice that stopped the twinkling of the stars:

"Ye vile beasts, ain't ye 'shamed fer to attack animals that never did ye harm?"

The wolves stopped howling, the sheep stopped bleating, the cows stopped bellowing, and the horses stopped neighing. It was so silent you could hear the moon moving. Ethan stared at the wolves for a time, and so strong was the look in his eyes, they sat up on their haunches with hanging tongues and just couldn't make a sound.

Then he preached them a sermon stronger than the preacher preached Sunday in church. He told them what a terrible thing it was to kill a poor bleating sheep, or scare to death a kind cow who had no way to defend herself. He told these wolves many more things besides. But the wolves had got used to the roaring voice; they dropped from their haunches, and fire flew from their eyes; they snarled mean, and their tails switched swiftly.

That raised Ethan's dander high as Mount Washington. He lifted his voice so strong it made the frozen pines shake, and told those wolves to make themselves scarce or he would get at them with his ax, and they'd soon look like crushed blackberries in the snow.

Now the wolves understood Ethan's words, and they stopped in their tracks. But still they would not go away.

Then Ethan just took one step outside the door, and that was enough.

The wolves hung their heads, dropped their tails, and slunk away, looking backward now and then. When Ethan saw this, he went back to his warm bed.

"Told ye, Nate, I'd get rid o' them wolves without gun or cudgel. They've gone. D'ye hear anythin'?"

But the night was silent, and the animals were quiet, and the two men went to sleep dreaming of warm food and happy summer.

The morning came bright and clear, and Ethan and Nate went out in the crunching snow. The sight of such great, white, snow-beauty made by God made them stand still for a time in prayer. Then they walked behind the stable toward the road and saw a great big hole in the ground where Ethan had hidden bear meat for winter's use. It was all gone save for a few bones. Ethan stopped and scowled with anger, but soon a smile came on his big, broad face.

Said Nate:

"I see the wolves didn't go empty from your place, Eth'. Preachin' didn't help much."

"There was good fat bear meat hid in that hole for winter use, an' they ate it, but every beast on earth must have its eatin', an' since they didn't kill wantonly, I'll forgive 'em." So spoke Ethan, the Giant of the Hills, with a great ringing laugh.

And Nate went away telling all and everyone that Ethan Allen Crawford, the seven-foot Giant of the Hills, was good to beasts and even to wolves when they were not too mean and murderous.

Becky's Garden

A RICH Squire and his three daughters lived in a white house on a big lake in the White Mountains. The oldest daughter was beautiful, the second was pretty with a pert little nose, and the youngest, whose name was Becky, was just nice and shy.

That's what all the neighbors saw and knew, but what they didn't see and what they didn't know was that the oldest was greedy and mean, the second jealous and lazy, and the youngest kind and modest.

Not far from the Squire there lived a fine young fellow. He had a wide farm, fat cattle, strong horses, and was as handsome as handsome could be to boot. Every young maid living near and far had an eye on him and would have married him quicker than turning a heel, but quickest of all the three sisters. The oldest and the middle one said this without shame and fanfare, but the youngest just thought it and kept counsel to herself.

Now this winsome young man came often to the

house of the rich Squire, for he had a mind to marry one of the three maidens but he couldn't make up his mind which one he really wanted.

One evening he came for a little tell, and the sisters spoke of this and that and what each wanted most in the wide world, as is the way of the young.

The oldest said that what she wanted most was to live in a great city, wearing rich clothes and silken slippers. The middle one, she desired everything the oldest asked for and more to boot, like slaves and silver plates, a great mansion, and a carriage and four horses. When it was the turn of the youngest, she said she desired most of all a garden filled with flowers even more beautiful than she now grew, and the cows far, far away so they wouldn't trample upon them. For Becky loved flowers above everything else she had.

The young fellow went home late that night, in deep thought, trying to decide which of the three sisters would make him the best wife, but he could not make up his mind.

When the three daughters were alone with their father, the Squire said to Becky:

"Daughter mine, do you really love flowers so dearly?"

"That I do indeed, and I wish I had a garden where the cows wouldn't lay waste the little flowers with their hoofs. I want to cry when I see them crunched and crushed deep in the ground."

"That I can easily remedy," said the kind father. "I

have many islands on the lake, the most beautiful lake in the world. Choose the one you like best and plant your garden on it. No cows'll come there to crush or trample on your flowers."

No sooner did her two sisters hear this than they raised a hue and cry, shouting their father always favored Becky because she was the youngest, and that they were older, and as good as she.

The father listened for a time; then he said:

"Daughters mine, you can each have an island if you wish, but, since Becky asked before you did, she can be the first to choose."

The sisters did not like this, for they were sure Becky would ask for the largest island on the lake, but what could they say? As for the father, he did not care if Becky did ask for the largest of his islands. She never asked for rich clothes or shiny jewels as the others did.

"Now, Becky, daughter mine," said he, "I have twenty-one beautiful islands, each one like a jewel in the lake. Choose the one you want."

For a time Becky was silent; then she said:

"I want the smallest island of all you have, father dear. Just enough for a little garden."

The older sisters opened their eyes wide as pie plates; even the father was so surprised he was silent for a while. Then he spoke:

"Is that truly all you want, daughter mine? The smallest island of all?"

"That is all I want," said she.

"By piggins and noggins you're a strange little girl, and you can have the smallest island if that is what you want. I'll give you the island that is just a dot of an island. Now, which ones do you, my elder daughters, want? First the oldest as is the custom."

"If Becky's a fool, I'm not," said she, tossing her head high in the air. "I want the biggest island of all those you have, father."

"The biggest of all my islands you shall have," said he.

The middle daughter made a wry face and asked for the next largest, and she got it.

The tale spread far, the tale of the islands and how each daughter made her choice.

Some thought Becky silly for having asked for the smallest when she might have asked for the largest; but most people said the opposite. They said she was a modest maiden and wise as well, for she had no big eyes which often bring big trouble. 'Twas much simpler to tend a small island than a large one full of big trees and wild prowling animals. She was the right maid for a wife to the best man in the land.

The young fellow, too, heard the tale of Becky's garden, as people called the little island now. He listened well and thought right smart, and it didn't take him long to know which one of the sisters would make the best wife for him.

So he came to the father and asked for Becky's hand, and the two were married and lived happily ever after.

As for Becky's sisters, they became meaner and greedier with the years, and in the end they were so mean and greedy that none would marry either of the two. Would you?

Old Ave Henry
and the Smart Logger Man

OLD Ave Henry was the hardest, smartest, meanest, cheatin'st, richest lumberman that ever was in all New Hampshire. He was a proud man, too, and wore a white shirt and a diamond pin in his tie except on days when he was mad. Then he wore an old blue cap and a gray old coat and men and beasts would keep out of his way.

But with all his smartness and cheating he'd sometimes get the short end of the stick, and it served him mighty right.

One day Slim, a six-foot logger, left his silver watch with Old Ave Henry while he went cutting his giant pines, oaks, and hemlocks. Came the end of the month, Slim returned to get his pay and his silver watch.

The rich lumberman paid him his wage but raged up and down shouting he never saw or heard of any silver watch. Well, what could a logger man do against a rich lumberman! No one could do anything against Old Ave

Henry in Lincoln town, for he owned it body, boots, and breeches.

Slim went off in great anger, telling everyone as far as Boston how the rich lumberman had cheated him of his watch.

Now it so happened that right at that very time Old Ave Henry had to cut miles and miles of logs for the railroad men to make railroad ties. So the lumber king sent word to Boston to hire all and everyone to come logging up Lincoln way for money. Slim was there and heard it too, he and his friend Johnny Zeke, to whom he was telling right then that Old Ave Henry'd steal the shell of a dried old acorn on the road.

Now Johnny Zeke was smart as a whip, slick as an otter, and not afeared of anything standing or creeping. He promised Slim he'd go up to the rich lumberman and find a way to repay Ave with interest for keeping the watch.

Johnny Zeke packed his bundle and started for Lincoln town, and since he loved a funny tale, a fine meal, and a clever trick, he was welcome in the farmhouses on the road. So, stopping often on the way, he came up to Old Ave Henry, who was hiring all the men he could find.

Johnny told the lumberman he had come from Boston for to work for him, cutting trees.

"Took ye a mighty long time to come from Boston," Old Ave Henry said, sneering-like. "I sent word full three weeks ago, and many men have come afore ye."

"Oh, Mister Henry, the sun was bright, an' people were good t' me on the way," said Johnny Zeke, laughing and showing his big yellow teeth.

"So that's the kind of fellow y'are. Now ye kin keep busy countin' the railroad ties from Lincoln up to Boston. Ye're jest the right and proper man for it."

He laughed aloud, and so did the other men who were in the room, for they all knew that Old Ave was only joking.

Johnny laughed too and said:

"Thank ye, Mister Henry. I think I kin do that fer ye."

Johnny Zeke went to the railroad station at Lincoln and walked on the road bed and began counting railroad ties. He counted each and every one of those wooden ties till he came to Boston by the sea, where he met Slim.

"Slim, ye come back wi' me to Old Ave Henry an' watch the trick I played on him. It'll give ye a good laugh that'll make a fine salve to heal the soreness 'bout your silver watch."

So the two went back, counting the railroad ties once again to make certain they had the right number, until they came to Lincoln.

It was Saturday eve, and Johnny and Slim went straight to Old Ave Henry's office where he was sitting afore his big table in his white shirt with a big diamond pin in his tie. The room was full of men getting their pay for the week's work.

"Mister Henry," said Johnny Zeke in a booming voice, "I've counted all the railroad ties from here to Boston, an', to make sure, I counted 'em back again. I've got the number, an' I've got Slim, who walked all the way with me to prove I did it honest."

At first Old Ave Henry just couldn't speak; then he roared:

"Ye're out of your head, ye corn-ribbed fool. I was only jestin'."

"Ye didn't say so, Ave Henry. Ye told me t'count the ties from here to Boston, an' count every one of these ties from here to Boston I did. Now pay me fer two weeks' work. I've witnesses," and he pointed to the men who had been in the room when Old Ave Henry told Johnny Zeke to count ties.

What could Old Ave Henry say? Here was a fellow who had got the best of him for once. Everyone laughed, but the lumber king made a sour face and paid Johnny Zeke for counting ties.

The tale spread far and wide. I heard it once, I heard it twice, and now you've heard it, too.

VERMONT

The Green Mountain State

Troy

Rutland

Bennington

Brattleboro

Lucky Rose Tuttle

IN all Vermont, from Troy to Brattleboro, there was no one kinder or more thriving than Rose Tuttle. Some said it was because she always wore a bit of mountain ash, which brings luck, around her neck.

Rose Tuttle was neither young nor old, neither pretty nor ugly, just a country girl with blue eyes and sunburnt cheeks who minded her own business and never gossiped. From bright morning to cool evening she was busy working in her little house and on her little farm. For there were sights and sights of things to do. She did the hoeing and planting, and she tended the flowers. Sweet marjorams, mint, thyme, dahlias, marigolds, and delphiniums grew in her garden. There was not a farm or house in all Vermont more spick and span than Rose Tuttle's. It was indeed a pity that there was no one to share it with her. She wished for company.

But Rose Tuttle wasn't given to sighing and wishing; she was too busy for that. She tripped along the grass-grown path to the red painted barn to feed the little red hens and the red rooster. The early spring wind sang in

79

the leafless branches, whssssss! The sun shone on the brook which gurgled quickly, grl-grl-grl! But when she came near the barn door she stopped in great surprise at a most surprising sight.

There, right before her eyes, sat a banded rattler on his eight-rattle tail, weeping bitter tears. His skin was sulphur yellow, and black and brown velvety bands crossed each other all over him. A little below his head there was a big round bulge in his skin.

"Dear me!" said Rose Tuttle. "It's queer to see a rattler so early in the morning, weeping. What ails you?"

"Oh," said the rattler, "kind Rose Tuttle, I just woke up from my long winter's sleep. I was very hungry and couldn't find any rabbits or rats, or mice or birds. So I came to your chicken coop to eat an egg or two and swallowed by mistake the glass egg you left for your hens. It won't go up, it won't go down, and it won't melt!" The poor rattlesnake wept harder than ever.

"Well, of all things! Serves you right," said Rose Tuttle. "I suppose I shouldn't help you, but I don't like to see a body sufferin'."

She picked up two stones and very carefully crushed the glass egg. You can just imagine how happy the banded rattler was when this was done! He wriggled his body and rattled his rattles.

"Now, what can I do for you?" asked the grateful snake.

"You don't have to do a thing for me," said Rose

Tuttle. "Unless you would like to lie in front of my house and stop the peddlers of Montpelier and of Brattleboro from coming up my clean steps and making them dirty. Just rattle your rattles, and I'll come and buy what I want outside."

"That I'll do gladly," said the banded rattler.

So the rattler sat in front of the house all day long listening to Rose Tuttle singing as she worked. But when a peddler from Montpelier or a peddler from Brattleboro came near, the banded rattler would rattle angrily and the peddler would stop. Rose Tuttle would come out at the sound and do her buying before the steps.

One morning Rose Tuttle took a walk in the woods to see how much maple sap there was in the wooden troughs hanging under the maple trees. She put on her shawl and walked under the spruce and hemlock trees, under the long-needled pines and the paper birches. There was a cool wind and a warm sun, and the brooks were singing. Suddenly she heard a different sound, a coughing and whining, a wheezing and sneezing. She came to a clearing, and there she saw a little bear sneezing and coughing. Big tears rolled down his shaggy brown fur.

Rose stopped in great surprise.

"Now, what ails you?" she asked.

"Oh, I, zh! zh! zh! got up too soon from my winter sleep and I've caught a terrible cold in my chest and eyes. My head hurts, my back hurts, and my legs hurt so I can't walk."

"Now, that's a pity, indeed," said Rose, "but I know

just how to cure you. Come to my little house."

"Oh, I can't walk," said the little bear between whimpering and wheezing.

"Then I must carry you," said Rose Tuttle. So she picked up the little bear in her arms just as if he were a baby and carried him home. She brought the baby bear into the little sitting-room-dining-room-kitchen. There she laid him down on the maple sofa and tucked him in with shawls and braided woolen mats, homemade blankets and home-woven blue wool coverlets. The sizzling pine logs in the fireplace smelled like perfume, and the water boiling in an iron pot on the iron hook made a nice song. The little bear felt warm and happy.

Rose Tuttle gave him a hot sweet-smelling drink of herbs, and his pain was quickly gone. In three days he was up and well, ready to go back to his brothers and sisters in the woods.

"I'd like to do something for you," growled the little bear.

"I only did what anyone would do," Rose Tuttle said. "Well, if you must, come and visit me sometimes, for it is lonely when I'm not busy, and I do hanker so to see somebody."

"Why don't you have a husband?" growled the little bear.

"Well, it would be nice to have someone share the work and comfort of my home," said Rose Tuttle.

"Then I know what I can do for you," said the little bear. "I heard my mother say that the village schoolmaster is much in need of a wife. He is always forgetting things and never eats enough. He's the right man for you."

"He would suit me well," Rose said. "And don't forget the parson."

"I'll not," growled the baby bear, cured of his cold and aches.

From that day Rose Tuttle sang more loudly and worked harder. The hens noticed it, and so did Pompey, the dog, and Jerusha, the cow, and they were all glad, for they loved their mistress dearly.

The weeks went by until one day, when a cricket was singing on the hearth, there was a great noise outside, and the banded rattler rattled merrily. Rose Tuttle ran out to see. There was the baby bear leading Abner, the schoolmaster, dressed in his Sunday clothes. The mother bear was leading Parson Pennington.

"Here's kind Rose Tuttle," said the baby bear. "She wears a bit of mountain ash about her neck, which means luck."

"Marry them at once, Parson Pennington," growled the mother bear, "so that their luck may go on together."

Abner looked at Rose Tuttle and saw her bright eyes and kind smile, and said, "Well, I could do worse."

So Parson Pennington married them, and there was a great feast, and they all lived happily ever after, because Rose Tuttle wore a bit of mountain ash and was kind to every living creature.

The Devil in the Barrel

YEARS ago, there lived in the White Marble State of Vermont a great preacher, a strange preacher. Lorenzo Dow was his name, and when he preached the good word it was like all the winds of creation roaring in all the trees of America. And the holy words made men good and made them repent.

One wild winter's night, when the heavens were spitting snow fit to pierce animals' hides, Lorenzo Dow, the great preacher, the strange preacher, walked blindly along the road till he came to a log house where he saw a light. He knocked on the door, and he knocked again and again. After he knocked a long time, the farm woman who lived there opened the latch, and the preacher asked for a night's lodging.

"My husband's away in the tavern talking politics, and there's little room in the house."

"I'm a man o' God, preaching the holy word, and I need only a little room. Surely you'll not turn me away in this blinding storm," he shouted above the wind.

"My husband's a godless man, an' the sight o' preachers makes 'm mad."

"I've dealt with godless men before, and I've no fear of your husband. Let me stay for the night, mistress, and the Lord'll reward you for it."

What could the woman do? The storm was raging, and no decent body could turn anyone away from the door, leastways a preacher.

So, she let him enter and put him where wood and tools were kept. It was a chamber shut off from the large room by thin planks full of cracks.

"Stay there quietly till the mornin', an' my husband'll never know ye're here," she said.

Lorenzo Dow, tired as a snail from the day's walking, said his prayers, lay down, and soon was sound asleep. But he did not sleep for long.

Suddenly there was a pounding and a knocking at the door! He awoke and heard through the chinks a pawky young farmer neighbor, Caleb by name, ask to come in and rest before going home.

The farmer woman let him in quick as jumping crickets, and after a little talk she made him tea and gave him cake.

"I'd have ye stay for the night," said she, "only my husband's coming soon an' seein' guests'll raise a rumpus to lift the roof. The best thing for ye's to go as soon as ye've warmed your inners a bit."

So they talked and talked, and maybe they'd still be talking, when for the third time there was a knocking and banging at the door loud enough to wake the Seven Sleepers.

"Open the door an' open quick. It's me, yer husband. The snow's cuttin' holes in my face. Open quick," and he kicked the door harder than a mule.

"Land o' goshen," cried the farmer woman, "it's my husband!" and she thought fast as lightning. "Can't keep him out there, Caleb, an' if he sees ye, millstones'll be flyin'." She looked around and saw a barrel full of tow.

"Quick, Caleb," she cried, "jump in the barrel an' I'll cover ye with the tow. When he goes to sleep ye kin go. No use arguin' with my husband at this hour."

Caleb jumped into the barrel, and the farmer's wife covered him with tow so you couldn't see him if you tried.

Then she opened the door, and her husband came in, red as embers, ranting up and down worse than the storm outside.

In the end the woman couldn't stand it any more, and she said:

"Ye must be still; there's Lorenzo Dow the great preacher weary an' tired a-sleeping in the woodshed. Have respect for a man o' God." She thought that would keep him quiet.

"I've no respect fer any preacher, an' in my house I'm king o' the roost. So ye let Lorenzo Dow in my house when ye know I don't like the sight o' preachers! I've never seen his face, but maybe I'd like to see it once so I kin tell him he can't put religion in me nor kin he

scare me with the Devil. Ho there, preacher!" he roared.
"Ho there, black crow, come in here and let me hear
yer crowin'."

He thumped and thwacked, and the boards of the
house shook with fear. Soon the great preacher, the
strange preacher, came in.

"Ho there!" bellowed the farmer. "Heard it said ye
kin put good in sinners' hearts an' raise the Devil fer
punishment. Ye can't put anythin' in my heart an' ye
sure can't raise the Devil to punish me."

"Yes I can," roared Lorenzo Dow even louder. "I
preach the word of the Almighty, thawin' icy hearts o'
sinners, and if I can't do it that-a-way, I call in the Devil
to burn the sinners' flesh on hickory wood till the day
o' black doom."

"Moon talk," shouted the farmer. "Just words runnin' loose. Ye can't frighten me with such tales."

"What if I show ye the Devil right here in a roarin'
flame o' Hell-fire?"

"Ye can't," said the farmer.

"What if I do?" said Lorenzo Dow.

"I say again ye can't."

"If I raise the Devil now before yer sinful eyes, will
ye stop goin' to the tavern and come to meetin' and pray
to the Lord?"

"Ye can't raise the Devil, I says."

"Will ye promise ye'll stop running to the tavern and
go to prayer if I do?"

"I'll promise anythin', fer I know ye can't do it."

"Your word on the book o' the Lord!"

"I'll swear," said the farmer.

"I'll now raise the Evil One before yer very eyes," said Lorenzo Dow, the great preacher, the strange preacher, "and ye must keep yer promise. But open the door wide, for the Devil'll come in a flame o' Hell-fire and needs plenty o' space, lest ye want yer house burnt down this fierce and snowy night. And don't forget the vow ye swore!"

The farmer tore the door wide open, and Lorenzo Dow took the lighted candle from the table and put it in the tow sticking from the barrel.

The flame of the burning tow leaped high, but still higher leaped young Caleb, who was in the barrel. He rushed out like Indians beating bullets, all a-fire, into the driving snow and quickly disappeared, none the worse for the little burning warmth.

The farmer stood frozen still, the farmer's wife never said a word though her mouth was wide open, but Lorenzo Dow, the strange preacher, the great preacher, said enough.

"Miserable sinner!" he roared. "Close that door and never go to the tavern again. Pray to the Lord to forgive ye and come to every meetin' as ye said ye would."

That farmer never, never went to the tavern again from that day on. Instead he went to church and prayed harder than twelve deacons put together. And from then on he **was a** good man for the rest of his life.

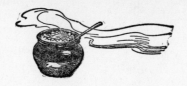

Green Mountain Hero

UP in the Green Mountains of Vermont, lived Colonel Ethan Allen. A bigger, better, stronger, fiercer fighting man there never was. He was tall as a maple, strong as an ox, fleet as a deer, and smart as a lynx. There wasn't a man he couldn't outshoot, outargue, outroar, and outfight. And he used the strength of his body and the power of his mind to beat the Britishers of New York who were trying to cut off a piece of good Vermont State. For that reason the Yorkers had offered a big sum of money to anyone who would capture him.

One evening he went to meet Eli, his captain, to talk about more ways of teaching the Yorkers of New York the proper boundary lines. He swung along the giant pines, the hemlocks, great oaks, maples, and ash. The sweet smell of trees and leaves and the dance of the stars in the sky made him feel that his own state was Paradise here on earth.

Suddenly a fierce catamount high up on a tree leaped down on his back. Ethan just turned around, looked into the fiery eyes, and let out a blood-curdling greeting louder than the loudest panther. At the same time he got hold of the beast by the neck and flung it high and flung it low and flung it all around against bushes and trees, till the body just hung limp and loose in his strong hands. Then he flung it away just as he would a bone.

On he went whistling a tune gaily, for he felt just right. Whippoorwills were crying, and birds were screaming, and Ethan thought he'd join in the gay chorus, so he let out three hooting screeches of an owl. He did it again and again. For that was the sign by which Ethan called the Green Mountain Boys who fought for state and for country. So perfectly did Ethan screech that a big grumpy owl, sitting near by, thought it was a bird ready to attack his mate, and he flew wildly at Ethan, screeching and scratching. But Ethan flapped his big arms all around, and the bird flew off, frightened. Ethan laughed and went his way still hooting like an owl.

Suddenly there came from way off three hoots of another owl, three times, one after the other. Not as good as Ethan's but still like an owl. Ethan answered, Eli came to him, and the two went along talking.

So they came to the house of Master Richards and his wife, who were their friends.

The good people greeted them warmly, and soon all were feasting on beefsteak with ham, mutton, and pies, washing it down with cold, yellow cider. There were tales and talk, and they all had a merry time—never

dreaming that spies had told the British soldiers up in
Crown Point just where Ethan was.

Master Richards was telling Ethan and his friend they
were safe as Heaven in his house when there was a banging and battering at the door.

"Who's there?" roared Master Richards.

"Soldiers of the Crown, to capture Ethan Allen who's
within."

Ethan and Eli leaped up ready for defense, but smart
Mistress Richards said quickly, "There's more than one
way to skin a cat. Run up to the attic chamber, put your
guns against the window and your caps on them, then
wait till you hear from me. I'll take care of these
fellows."

Master Richards opened the door, and six British soldiers came in armed to the teeth.

"Where's Ethan and Eli?" said the leader. "We know
they're here."

"They're here and ready for ye to take, gentlemen,"
said Mistress Richards, "but where's the hurry? They're
up in the atttic eating and drinking, and soon they'll
have so much o' both ye can capture them without a
scratch or lick. Ye know the tales of strength of Ethan
Allen. Besides, here's a feast ye've not had in a long time,
I'm certain. Why not join in our meal? Come, Ethan
and Eli are up there safe enough. Ye kin see them sitting
near the window. Just watch 'em and eat your fill; then
take 'em at your leisure."

The meats and drink on the table looked mighty

tempting, and the captain saw the two coon caps near the window.

"We might as well eat, good lady, before we capture the rebels," he said gaily. So they all sat down, the six of them, and ate and drank and sang British songs while every now and then a soldier went out to see if Ethan and Eli were still sitting safe, their furry caps against the window. Each time they looked the caps were still there.

Meanwhile, the good hostess, Mistress Richards, was busy running back and forth bringing pitchers of pale cider, meat, and bread—and every now and then she'd run up to Ethan and Eli to post them how the land lay.

So it went on for a time until Mistress Richards came up to Ethan and said:

"Now they are deep in their cups, and I think ye can come down one at a time and go out without being noticed."

First Ethan came, slowly, stealthily, his body close to the wall—and quickly was out through the kitchen door.

But the caps were still hanging on the guns when an enemy soldier came out to take another look.

Then after a little time Eli came down cautiously, his body close to the wooden wall, and walked out through the kitchen door.

Not a soldier had noticed them. Their eyes were heavy, and their voices were thick.

Both Ethan and Eli waited in the shadow below the trees, and soon Mistress Richards lowered the weapons and caps through the window, whispering for them to hear:

"Be off quickly; take my husband's mare. She's strong and kin carry ye both. When ye get to Simon's farm, borrow another horse, and may luck go wi' ye."

Ethan and Eli went to the stall and took out the mare, but, when they came out, there stood a great white stallion pawing the grassy earth restlessly. His neck was high, and his tail was straight, and the wind blew the white mane in the silvery moonlight so that it looked like magic white silver.

"Wonder where the horse came from," whispered Eli.

"It came from the high hills of Vermont. I've seen it often in the morning standing against the blue, ruler of the wind and sky. Some day I'll be a white stallion, too, in the Green Mountains, snorting and whinnying, and ranging all over the land Yorkers want and will never get."

Up both leaped and soon were off at a pace the British soldiers could never follow.

Even if they wanted to they couldn't, those six soldiers in Mistress Richards' house. They had drunk and eaten so much they weren't fit for anything.

When they saw the caps were no more in the window, they raised a hue and cry. They rushed up the stairs and found an empty chamber. The birds had flown, and they spoke bitterly to Mistress Richards.

But she was sweet and smiling and said:

"Good soldiers, Ethan and Eli escaped through no fault of mine. If they hadn't, and ye'd arrested 'em, the Green Mountain Boys'd soon have the red cock reigning in my house. Fighting, pillaging, and burning is your business; mine is to prevent it. Ye've eaten and drunk and made merry, and no man is hurt. What more do ye want?"

The soldiers went off grumbling.

Mistress Richards went off smiling, and Ethan and Eli went off to do great deeds for state and country.

The Ride in the Night

OLD Pete was a stingy man. He squeezed pennies'
eagles black and blue before letting them go; he ate only
a crumb at a time to save his food, and that's not spinning a yarn. But he was even stingier about his watermelons. He said he was the first man to bring melons up
to cold Vermont, and he wasn't going to let any man,
woman, or child so much as touch them. And that made
every man, woman, and child, boy and girl, just about
as crisscross as they could be. For you know how
'most everybody, and boys and girls in particular, love
watermelons—about as much as horses love sugar.

But that made no difference to Old Pete, not to him.
He'd never give a piece of melon to a living person.
He'd keep them to himself, though he needed that many
melons no more than a dog needs two tails hanging
from his back.

One morning just one melon, one out of thirty-seven
long, large, fat melons, was missing from his melon
patch. Maybe an animal ate it; maybe it wasn't an animal

on four legs; no matter. Old Pete made a rumpus to raise the Heaven higher than the Holy Lord himself. He ranted up and down the village street accusing this one and that one and every mother's son of stealing that melon. And he said from that night on he'd be watching that melon patch with his gun on his knees. And, from that night on, there he was up on the hill watching his melon patch, his gun on his knees.

That made everybody in the village madder than wet hens. There wasn't a one from the minister down didn't think all the melons should be taken from that patch to teach Old Pete the Christian way of living with good neighbors. Some said they were ready to do it—maybe the first night the moon hid behind the clouds. They were watching just the same as Old Pete.

But the miser never heeded the talk. Night after night he hitched up his oxen to the old wagon, put straw in it, filled the green bottle he called "Green Betty" with good, yellow, hard cider, took his old gun, and drove up the hill to the melon patch.

It was a long way. First he'd drive around the barn, then along the road to the mud pond that was pretty deep. Then he'd drive up the steep hill to the top where the melon patch was.

When he got to it, he'd let the oxen loose in the pasture and set himself humpbacked in the warm straw, watching and waiting.

One night, when the clouds rode low hiding the moon, some good fellows of the village thought it was the right and proper night to teach Old Pete a lesson in neighborliness. There were four of them—Ziba Tut, Wait Baimiss, Abel Brown, Jehu Watt—four lusty, young fellows ready for weal or woe. After the lights were out and people abed, the four walked to the muddy frog pond and then up the hill where Old Pete was sitting in the straw.

Now, while they were walking Pete was busy with Green Betty, for the air was a mite cold. The peepers peeping and the wind dancing made a little music that sounded good. 'Twasn't bad at all to be resting warm with Green Betty and the music. So Old Pete closed his eyes just for a minute now and then. Next he turned on the right side looking down the hill. There wasn't a body there. Why, just knowing Old Pete was there with his trusty gun would keep the riffraff from coming near his fine ripe melons. He closed his eyes now and then for a little longer, then still a little longer. His head rested snug as a bug in that straw, and 'twas much easier to keep eyes closed than open—just a little longer . . . longer. . . . Then Old Pete's eyes were closed and didn't open any more. Instead, his mouth was wide, wide open. And from his wide open mouth came a different kind of music from that the peepers and wind were making. 'Twas more like the music from a buzz saw. Snores! Steady snoring! Steady without stopping, just as the peepers were peeping without stopping.

Just about then Ziba Tut, Wait Baimiss, Abel Brown, Jehu Watt came up the hill for fun and frolic. They came cautiously and quietly to be greeted by the snoring music.

"Gosh all fishhooks! A snorin' man can't fire a gun, kin he?" said Ziba Tut.

"He can't fire no gun and he can't see if ye take his melons," spoke Wait.

"If we could take that miser out o' the wagon, take all the melons, an' drive 'em away in his own wagon wi' his own oxen, 't 'd be jest the right and proper punishment for that old skinflint," said Abel.

"Hold on, fellows," said Jehu, "I b'lieve I got a better way to fix Old Pete so he'll be good from now on till Kingdom Come. Tell ye what, let's roll 'm down the hill into that muddy ol' pond and then tell 'm it's the Devil's doin' for hoardin' his melons 'stead o' sharin' 'em with friends and neighbors."

The others thought that was a fine plan. So they quietly pushed the wagon downward toward the hill and then gave it a gentle push and let it roll down.

The hill was long and steep. First Old Pete rolled slowly, then faster, then faster and faster and faster. Old Pete, he woke up all of a sudden and didn't know where he was. He really thought Old Nick was a-pushing him down. Suddenly, when the rolling wagon was near the pond, it hit a stump! Pete flew into the muddy water with a splash and a cry, Green Betty flew against a tree and crashed and cracked into a thousand pieces.

Old Pete sat up to his neck in the muddy water not knowing what to do, when he saw coming from the opposite side Ziba, Wait, Abel, and Jehu. They had quickly run around the hill to come the other way.

Cried Ziba Tut:

"We saw on the road a tall, tawny black fellow with horns on his head an' a green bottle in his hand all smellin' o' brimstone. He told us we'd find ye in the pond ready to share yer melons with all, and never drink cider again."

Wait Baimiss said it too and so did Abel Brown and Jehu Watt, and when four say the same thing, no man in all the State of Vermont could doubt it.

They took Old Pete from the pond and brought him home, and from that day on he was a very good man. He never touched a drop of hard cider and shared his melons with all his neighbors—as a good neighbor should. Most of all he shared it with boys and girls of the village, who loved red, cool, juicy watermelon on a summer's day. Just the same as you and I.

The Tale of the Tail of a Bear

IN the early time, it was bear-time in Vermont. There were more bears up around the Green Mountains than in any other state from north to south, and the pioneers and settlers, men and women, boys and girls, had their hands and homes full of the big hairy beasts.

There are many tales about the bears of those bear days, and some are sad and some are not sad at all. Here's a tale of the tail of a bear, and you'll soon know whether it'll bring tears to your eyes or laughter to your face.

There was a man named John in Vermont, whose wife one day asked him to go to town to get her needles and thread, sugar and salt, and many other things besides. So he and his neighbor James took a boat and went by way of Chimney Point to fetch the things that bring cheer and comfort to the home.

They rowed along the waters of the great dancing lake and suddenly saw afar a big swimming thing.

"It's a deer!" cried James.

"It looks as if it might be," said John, "and we can use meat and hide well enough."

They turned their boat and swiftly paddled toward the beast, but, when they got nearer, they saw it was no deer at all—but a giant she-bear paddling slowly in the water, sort of pleasant-like.

"Bear meat is just as good as deer meat, and a bear's pelt is the warmest thing I know on a cold winter night," said John.

"But we have no gun," said James ruefully.

"We have an ax," said John. "Now, James, you row alongside of the animal while I hit her on the head with the ax."

In a few strokes the boat glided alongside the big bear.

John raised the ax high and brought it down as heavily as he could, plunk! on the bear's head. But this was a bear of bears, maybe the strongest, smartest bear in all Vermont. The heavy blow of the ax bothered the beast no more than a dropping apple from a tree. She just turned her face, looked at them, opened her mouth grinning-like, and paddled along a little faster. That made John mad. Again he raised his ax and brought it down with all his might. But, not judging his distance as he had before, he hit the bear's tail instead, this time with the sharp side, cutting a gash which began to bleed. It angered the giant bear just a little. She turned around and raised her paws and chug-plunk! hit the boat. It turned over, and both men were deep in the water together with the bear.

Do you think that bear bothered with John and James? Not one bit. She did not even look at them; it was just that kind of a bear. Instead, the animal climbed on the boat and laid its great big body across, watching the two coughing and spluttering men. And if a bear can laugh with might and main, that bear was doing it. She opened her jaws wide, turned her head from side to side, and shook her body up and down.

Once, and only once, John and James tried to get hold of the sides of the boat, but the bear just hit their hands with her great paw, and they didn't try again. So the two swam to shore as best they could and went their way, while the bear with the cut tail got off the boat, paddled to the shore, went into the woods, and jogged along a-thinking.

Now I told you this bear was a bear of bears, a bear who could think near as good as any man. She just kept a-thinking as she jogged along to the cave where her two young 'uns were playing. In the end she had thought out something that would teach John a lesson not to hit a bear, that never did him any harm, with an ax. She took her cubs and went off to find John's house.

The sun set, and the stars came out. The bear and her cubs were trotting along the leafy ground in the woods. Trot trot, trot trot, they kept on trotting on leaves, moss, and ferns, led by the smell of John, which, as you know, is to a beast in the woods of greater help than eyes are to a man. After a time the three bears came to the clearing where John's log house stood.

In the house was Mistress John with her children, never dreaming she'd have visitors that evening. She was sitting on a stool near the fireplace, watching the hanging kettle in which bubbling samp was cooking for the evening meal. On the rough wooden table stood a pitcher full of milk, and around were plates with wooden spoons.

Mistress John sang a little song to her babe and was just turning to the black kettle to ladle out the dancing samp, when she heard a funny noise at the furry blanket that served as a door to the house.

She turned around, and there stood a great big bear and two little cubs, one on each side, looking all around.

Mistress John, she did her thinking quick. She picked up her babe and cried to the others:

"Hurry up the ladder into the loft above."

The children scampered up as fast as they could; Mistress John followed with the babe and drew the ladder after her. Up above they all sat down on the wooden poles and looked through the chinks to see what the bears would do.

The big black bear came in with the two cubs close behind her. They looked and sniffed at this and that and looked and sniffed at everything. So they came to the rough wooden table, and the mother bear thought she'd first drink the milk. She stuck her snout deep in the pewter pitcher, but it wasn't wide enough and fell, the milk spilling all over. The little baby bears licked it up and thought it very good.

Next the great big mother bear came up to the kettle of samp that was still steaming and bubbling a little. It smelled good, and the mother bear wanted to taste it. In went her open snout, and she took a great big mess in her mouth and—jumped back and let out a fierce, spluttering growl! She shook her head, stamped her paws, and danced all around so that it shook the planks and rocked the rafters. The samp was burning hot, and the bear had burned her snout and tongue and mouth.

Up in the loft the children were shouting with glee and laughter at the dancing, growling bear. Mistress John also laughed till the tears ran down her face.

When the great big bear heard the laughing she became even angrier and ran up and down the room knocking down everything that came her way while the two baby bears sat down at the table watching their mother's strange behavior, not knowing just what to make of it.

The burning pain in the bear's mouth would not go away with all her running around, so she tried to get up to the loft from which the shouts of laughter came. She raised herself on her paws and tried to jump, but with all her trying she couldn't do it, so she sat down spluttering and pawing her mouth without end.

There they were, the three bears, the two little bears looking with their little eyes and the great big bear pawing and growling. A funnier sight there never was. The baby gurgled, and Mistress John and the children rolled on the poles with laughter. And as they rolled they pushed an old ax lying on the poles and it fell down through a wide chink . . . right on the mother bear's tail, right on the sore where the ax had cut her before.

The great big bear felt a sharp pain on the wound and stopped pawing and growling. Then the beast began thinking and wondering.

"John's ax is a fierce, magic ax. It followed me from the lake to his house and hit me now for the second time, and I'll not wait for the third time to be hit. Besides, John's home is a magic home where snout and tongue are burned without fire. It's no place for me or my cubs."

The great big mother bear rose and lumbered out of the cabin, the two cubs followed, and the children and mother John laughed and came down. When father John came home and heard the tale he laughed, too, and was very happy that nothing more had happened.

So ends the tale of the tail of the bear.

Well-Done-Peter-Parker

PETER PARKER was the biggest boaster in all of great Vermont. He could outboast a camp full of loggers spinning yarns around a cracked stove on a winter's night. He could tell bigger and better tales than any man that ever lived in all the Green Mountains, sure as brown beans. But no one from Stalbaus to Brattleboro believed a word he said, even though half of the things he told were true.

People only remembered the things that were not true. That is the way of people.

One fine day Peter Parker came back from the great war with a grand smile, a torn uniform, and chin music to beat bugles and drums. He smiled at every goodwife and girl, and they all smiled back at him. He spoke to every man and boy, and they made friends with him. So he came to the tavern, and there people feasted him and toasted him, and he told one and all that great General Washington had helped him, Peter Parker, win the war. The longer he stayed the more tales he told of battles he'd won and dangers he'd escaped, but most of all about the great giant British grenadier who had challenged him to a duel. 'Twas at a time when he was so busy knocking lobsterbacks right and left by the drove that he had no time to bother with just one single fellow.

"And here is the funny part o' my tale," said he, while young and old sat around listening with eyes and ears wide open. "Think on't. Just three days ago, scarce thirty miles from here, I met that very same great giant British grenadier who had challenged me to the duel, gaddin' about free as a deer. 'If the Continental Army didn't get ye, I, Peter Parker, will,' I cried to him. 'Now, I'll take up your challenge!'

"We were then in a tavern and made up we'd have it out right there and then on the hill beyond the town. Kith, kin, and caboodle, all came to see the great battle. They stayed below the hill so no one would be hurt. Then we set to work with gleamin' sabers. The fellow was seven feet tall, and I am just short o' six. He had a saber big as himself, but I made up in quickness and dexterity."

Peter Parker jumped up from his bench, leaped and cavorted about, and fought that battle all over again. He hacked and hammered with his arms showing how he fought, taking a lot of room for his big talk.

"Then," he roared in a voice of thunder, "I saw an opening, and with one clear cut of my trusty saber the head o' that boastin' British grenadier went off a-rollin' down the hill. And as that head rolled down the hill through brush an' grass, it shouted loud: 'Well done, Peter Parker! Well done, Peter Parker!'

"The crowd standing there took up the cry. Ye should have heard the shoutin' and hurrahin', but I didn't listen. Those praisin' words from my enemy touched my heart wi' pity. I ran after the head, quickly picked it up, and put it back on the shoulders. Then I smeared it with salve an Indian woman once gave me for savin' her only child. No sooner did that salve touch the flesh than it mended good as the day when the Lord made it. The people cheered clear to Heaven, all cryin': 'Well done, Peter Parker! Well done, Peter Parker!' "

There was shouting, stamping, laughing, and crying from all who heard the tale, and there was more drink and venison, and brown beans. All were gay and happy, for they felt the wars were over forever and the world would be at peace with men like Peter Parker watching it. So the evening wore on, and some of those present began going home.

Now amongst those were a few lusty fellows named Simon, Peter, and Zenes, and Zerah, who didn't believe a word Peter Parker said and thought him a coward besides. Maybe they were a little jealous, but whatever the reason they decided they'd find out if Peter Parker had the courage he said he had. They took a pair o' breeches and a velvet coat, a three-cornered hat and a pair of shoes, a hatchet and a bundle of hay, and walked along the path of hemlock, pine, and birch where they knew Peter Parker would come on his way home.

"We'll soon find out if Peter Parker is the worst boasting liar in our state or whether he isn't," said Simon.

"I don't think a word o' truth comes from his big mouth." That from Peter.

"There's more sense in cluckin' o' hens than in the blatherin' talk o' Peter Parker, and ye'll soon see it to boot," cried Zerah.

"Here's a good spot for testing Peter Parker's brassy blowin'," said Zenes.

They had come to a place where a tall maple stood right on the path.

"Here's where we hang him," said Zerah.

With the hatchet Simon carried they cut a forked branch off the tree and a straight one, tying them together crosswise. They put the breeches on the forked branch, the coat on the cross, the three-cornered hat on top, and the shoes at the end. Arms and legs they filled with hay and twigs till it was as good a scarecrow as was ever made in all the land.

Then they hung it on the maple tree so it dangled in the air. Simon tied a thin string in the middle and climbed on the nearest tree while the other three hid in the bushes.

A silver half-moon ran in the sky watching the merry game, and the stars shone lower to see it, too. The trees drew strange shadows on the ground, and birds and insects made music fit for spooky sport.

Soon a little song was heard from afar.

'Twas Peter Parker, full of good food and good pride as any soldier who had won a war would feel. He rolled along the road in an apple-peel gait a-singing:

> "As I went down to Derby
> All on a summer's day,
> 'Twas there I saw the biggest sheep,
> 'Twas ever fed on hay.

> "And sing tithery I reory ann,
> Sing tithery I o day."

Simon pulled the string so the hanging figure moved back and forth, back and forth. The song came nearer:

> "The wool on the sheep bag, sir,
> It reached unto the sky.
> The eagles built their nest there,
> And I heard the young ones cry.

> "And sing tithery I reory ann,
> Sing tithery I o day."

Right then Peter Parker came to the maple where the hanging man was swinging back and forth, back and forth.

Peter Parker had just begun the next verse of the fine Green Mountain song:

> "The wool on the belly, sir,
> It dragged unto the grrr . . ."

The word stuck in the middle of his throat and wouldn't come out. He wasn't frightened seeing that

dark man swinging from the tree, swinging back and forth, but he was surprised as you and I would be. The four conspirators, thinking Peter was scared, swelled with glee.

Suddenly Peter Parker roared in a voice to frighten bird and insect:

"What are ye, God, man, or Devil?"

The hanging man was silent, swinging back and forth, back and forth.

Roared Peter Parker once again:

"I ask ye again, are ye God, man, or Devil?"

The only answer the hanging man gave was to swing back and forth, back and forth.

"I say for the third and last time, and answer quick," roared Peter Parker red with anger, "are ye God, man, or Devil? An' if ye don't answer! . . ."

The hanging fellow just kept on swinging.

Now Peter Parker was fighting mad. He took his gun and began beating the rocking, hanging man.

"I'll soon find out if ye're God, man, or Devil," he shouted.

Right then the hanging man came down—kerplunk! and Peter Parker leaped on him to find . . . 'twas only a straw man! You should've seen his face!

"Devils and donkeys!" was all he could say. But quick the cool head of a soldier of the wars came to the fore. He took a good look at the clothes by the moonlight.

"Just what I need; my own clothes are torn and tattered," he cried aloud gaily. He took off the clothing from the sticks and went his way, finishing the fine Green Mountain song of the Derby Ram.

As for Simon, Peter, and Zenes, and Zerah, they went home, never a one opening his mouth. But like good Green Mountain Boys they quickly gave credit where credit was due.

They told the tale and said "Well-Done-Peter-Parker" truly deserved the name.

From that day on every man, woman, and child in the good marble State of Vermont believed every word "Well-Done-Peter-Parker" ever said.

MASSACHUSETTS
The Bay State

Ipswich

Salem

Boston

Plymouth

Cape Cod

The Strange Adventure
of the Cowboy-Sailor

THERE'S many a one knows about the whistling whale, the sulphur-yellow-green and purple sea-serpent with the six eyes, and the lady with the red-heeled slippers playing cards with Satan in person, inside the whale. But not many know what happened to all of 'em the night the moon and the stars splashed magic on the sea and the coast. Only a few "Old-Timers" know this, and I heard 'em tell it, and now I'll tell it to you.

That night, the magic of the moon and the stars was so strong it crept into the streets of a little village by the sea, and it was that very night Bowleg Bill, the cowboy-sailor, came back from Wyoming. He loved the sea as much as the sagebrush and couldn't live in either place without wanting to go to the other.

He tramped through the streets, past the houses, led by the magic salty smell, and soon stood deep in the sand listening to the galloping waves. He was there no more than a turn or two, when he saw afar off something in the white moonlight that made him rub his eyes till stars were jumping all around 'm. There was a long, fat, round something coming his way, weaving like prairie grass in a high wind at noon. But it wasn't soft and green, it was sulphur-yellow-green and purple. Soon he could see it was a snake, a sea-serpent-snake. On its head were two high moose antlers. There was an eye in between 'em and one on each side gleaming ruby red—and three eyes behind its neck shining like crackling fire of dry twigs.

"Bless my spurs if 'tain't the old sea-serpent. Howdy, an' what's itchin' ye, old salt rattler?"

The sea-serpent came right up to the beach, right where Bowleg Bill was standing in the sand. Bill took a good look at it, and it was sure worth looking at. You just couldn't think of anything prettier than that sea-going fish-horse. It had yellow-green and purple rings all over, and, when it wriggled along, the colors shone in the moon like rockets. Soon it bobbed along the edge of the water and said:

"Bill, let's go for a ride on the sea-prairie. I've got a little adventure for you."

Now Bowleg wasn't a man to refuse riding any animal any time, whether horse, serpent, or mountain lion.

Up he leaped, swinging himself through the air, landing eight feet from the neck of the sea-snake with the three flame-leaping eyes looking straight at him, friendly-like.

"A fine night for a ride in the sea," the sea-serpent said.

"Yippee-ee Hy-ee-ee—!" cried Bowleg. "Git along little dogie and show me if a sea-horse kin ride better 'n a mustang straight from Wyomin'."

"I'll show you!" shrieked the sea-animal gaily. Then that serpent began slithering through the dancing waves full fifty knots to the hour.

"Bowleg," the sea-horse said, after they had settled down to a steady pace, "Bowleg, I've kept a lookout for you for a long time, for there is a job on hand only you can do."

"And what's the job?" asked Bowleg, swaying from side to side while getting a manehold on the antlers.

"It's rescuing a lady. A lady that's wearing a jade-green taffeta dress, a paisley shawl around her shoulders, and red-heeled slippers on her feet. She's held captive inside a whale, and it'll be your job to get her out. No one can do it better than an eight-foot cowboy from Wyoming."

"I'm not much on ladies, pardner, but out my way we always rescue a lady in distress and ask no questions," and Bill swung his ten-gallon hat in a wide circle and elegantly bent forward. Then after a spell he said:

"Who is the lady with the red-heeled slippers an' the green taffeta dress?"

"Her name is Keziah, and she's been in that whale since the sea-cows came home. Old Scratch locked her in for the mean things she's done in her day, and every ten years he comes to play a game of cards with her. The stakes are always her freedom, and she always loses! But she's been there long enough now and has suffered long enough for her sins. It's high time to rescue her."

"Suits me fine," says Bill. "Ye jest keep on careenin' along, an' I'll do the rescuin'. I've got my six-shooter an' my trusty lariat, an' with 'em I'm ready for anythin' on water or on land."

So they went slithering and sliding, past fishes in schools and past fishes alone, past cuttlefish and codfish, past swordfish and flying fish.

Said Bowleg Bill:

"How much longer afore we get to the rescuin' party, pardner?"

"Pretty soon, pretty soon," the serpent-fish hissed. "Listen."

Bill listened sharply, and in between the singing of the wind he could hear a little tune now and then.

At first there were snatches of "Reuben Ranzo Was a Sailor." Then, as the sea-serpent kept on going, the tune became clearer, and soon he could hear it full clear— every note of it. It sounded as if it came from a deep, deep flute.

"I've heard this ditty before," said Bill, "an' it's a right smart tune, only we sing it different in the cow camps."

"Right you are, you sea-loving cowman, but Reuben Ranzo is Reuben Ranzo anyway you hear it."

They were now a full hundred miles out on the sea, and that's measuring thin. That magic of the silver moon and the golden stars was working strong on the swelling sea.

There, afar, Bowleg spied two great whales a-shining silvery-like in the moonlight. One was lying still as a schooner on a windless sea, and the other was rolling from side to side with the song coming clear from its spout. Clear like a fiddle in a dancing place.

"Thar she blows!" cried Bowleg.

"Aye, thar she blows! Only the blowing-singing the whale is doing is for the lady with the jade-green taffeta dress and the red-heeled slippers playing her ten-year game with the Devil himself. This is the little party I said I'd bring you to, Bill, and that's the lady we're going to save."

Then the sea-serpent slid alongside the whale that was lying still, and the cowboy-sailor saw a sight he had never seen before. He could look clear through the side of the whale.

There was a little room with a shiny sofa. Glass pictures hung on the walls, and scrimshaw and painted ships in green bottles stood on the mantel. A fancy whale lamp lit it all up so homelike you'd want to go in there yourself. In the middle was a round table covered with a tablecloth, and before it sat a perky lady with shiny black hair, dressed in a jade-green taffeta dress, a paisley shawl over her shoulders, and slippers with bright red heels on her feet. She sat straight as the back of her chair, holding five cards in her hand and looking square at a gentleman sitting as straight, across from her. He was elegantly dressed in black; two little horns stuck from his black hair, and two fiery eyes shone from his long face.

Bowleg Bill looked till his eyes near jumped from his head while the whale was blowing his tune and the lady and the gentleman inside were giving out cards and taking in cards, with neither one opening his mouth, only just playing.

"Come on, old sea-moose!" cried Bill. "I'll make a hitch in my rope, whip a loop, twirl it round, an' let it fly. Then we'll steer the critter straight to the beach, get the good oil, save the black-haired Miss, and burn Old Scratch. There's a night's work! I just can't abide seein' that lady inside o' a whale."

The sea-serpent wriggled a bit and said:

"You just watch and wait. Patience'll give you long life."

So they watched and waited while the whale played his ditty a little softer.

"Sorry, Keziah," they heard the gentleman say politely after a time. "Sorry, but you've lost again and must stay here another ten years. That's our agreement, isn't it?"

"Aye, I've lost," said she, just as polite but more icy—icy as the North Pole with a nor'wester blowing. "I've lost again, but one o' these days I'll beat ye as I've beaten every man that ever set himself 'gainst me."

"I'll give you another chance ten years from now, Keziah. Now I must be off to Boston town where many of my friends are waiting for my company," and he turned to the door.

"I'll get him when he comes out, sure as coyotes," Bowleg whispered hoarsely.

"Don't," the serpent whispered. "We're here to rescue the lady, not to catch the Devil."

The whale opened his mouth wide enough to swallow a dory, and the black-dressed gentleman came out, got on the back of the Whistling Whale, and away they went brimstone bent for the sea toward Boston town.

"Now we've got him out of the way," the sea-snake said, "and we can take care of the lady."

Then Bowleg Bill sang out:

"Yippee-ee Hy-ee-ee—! Lady Keziah, I've come straight from Wyomin' to the salty sea to rescue ye from the . . . D . . . oh, beg yer pardon—I mean the gent who just went away. I'm Bowleg Bill the sea-farin' cowboy from Wyomin', an' this is my friend the good sea-serpen' livin' in the sea. Ye kin oblige us an' jest come out o' your little hurrah nest an' mount this water-hoss. We'll take ye along to where the sea washes the sand or—to Wyomin'. Ye kin have yer own sweet choice."

For quite a spell Mistress Keziah looked at Bill with her cold black eyes, and then she spoke in her icy voice.

"Ye look like a mighty nice young man from the West, and I'm thankful for yer noble thought, but I like my little home, with none to ever bother me as they do in

Nantucket. Ye don't think I can't beat that cloven-footed fool at cards, do ye? Well, I can, but I don't wish to . . . and I let him think I can't. I lose my game as long as I wish and stay here as long as it pleases me. But I thank ye for your kindness."

Well, you could've bowled Bowleg Bill and the serpent over with a breath of air! And all the trouble they had taken! There was gratitude!

The lady mumbled something they couldn't understand, and the whale, with Mistress Keziah in her shiny taffeta dress and paisley shawl, was off.

"Well, I never could understand the female sex," said Bowleg Bill scratching his head.

And the sea-serpent added:

"My kind has dealt with women since Eden days, and we could never make out what a woman'll do next time. Sorry, Bill, had I known this I'd never have dragged you so far out. I thought we'd do a gallant rescuing deed."

"Well, don't worry yer head, old horse-wriggler. 'Twas a fine ride ye gave me, an' we both had a rip-roarin' time. Now take me back to Cape Cod shore, for I've got to find a berth with some good vessel."

So the sea-serpent-horse turned back, three eyes before, three eyes behind, and went at a clip of fifty fathoms to the hour, and that's a fact. It went past bluefish schools and big mackerel crowds, past haddock and eels and bearded walruses, for 'twas a night when the golden stars and the silver moon put magic on the foamy sea.

When they got near the sandy beach Bowleg Bill leaped fifty feet across the water, bidding his swaying sea-horse good night. And the serpent bade him the same, each going his way to find more adventure in the magic night.

The Golden Horse
with the Silver Mane

ONCE there was a boy, Peter by name, who loved
dreaming strange dreams and making rhymes, more than
playing Indians and sailors. Every day he sat high on
the ledge where the town church stood, watching to see
his father, Jacob, come home from the fields on a horse
seeming golden in the sun, with flying mane and tail of
fine-spun silver. He thought him a king from the Bible,
riding so, and he thought many other lovely things besides.

Sometimes the boy told his father of his dreams and
rhymes, but Jacob, who was a strict man walking in the
ways of God, did not like his son's talk. That was
witches' talk, he said.

But the mother did not think that. She understood the
boy Peter and called him her Dream Boy. She always
shielded him against her husband's scolding. So Peter
kept on seeing beauty where others did not, and kept on

dreaming dreams of things people could not understand.

One day he walked past the meeting green, along the river, until he reached the long salt grass. There he saw, lying on his back, a poorly dressed man counting the little white clouds in the bright blue sky and singing merrily:

> "Tirlery lorpin, the laverock sang,
>   So merrily pipes the sparrow,
> The cow broke loose, the rope ran home,
>   My fine boy, God give you good morrow."

Then he laughed aloud. Peter laughed too, and they were good friends at once.

"From where do you come? You are a stranger here," Peter said.

"I come from Nurembago, where the streets are lined with diamonds and rubies, and I travel up and down the woods and valleys, singing, eating, and sleeping, and right now I am very hungry."

"You have no home?"

"All the world is my home, and my house is where people let me rest."

"My father says every man should have a home."

"Your father is a fine man and wouldn't understand one like me. So I don't ask him to understand me and go my own way."

"I wish my father would understand when I tell him the rhymes I make and the adventures I have. But you do, don't you?"

"I do, most surely," the man replied leaning on his elbow.

"Each time my father goes to Salem or to Newbury I wait for him on the hill before the church, from where you can see far into the land. And when he comes riding in the sun his horse looks all shiny golden with a silver mane. He looks like a king in the Bible. I, too, have ridden on a golden horse with a silver mane and tail over mountains and seas. You believe me, don't you?"

"I believe you for certain, boy, for I often see men riding golden horses with silver manes and silver tails. You haven't a bit o' bread with you?" he asked.

"I have not, but come to my house, my mother'll find some for you."

So the two walked down the road until they came into the town. There they passed a house that had an outside oven from which came a sweet smell of steaming pudding.

"There's something good to eat!" the stranger said, sniffing the fragrant smell. "I'm certain this isn't the first pudding this goodwife is cooking, and I know she'll not mind if I just take a taste of it. I'll just take a little bit."

He took the pudding from the oven just as the good-wife came out to look at it. She began screaming at him. The noise scared him, and without thinking he began to run. So did Peter, and the goodwife after them crying, "Thief!"

"I'm no thief at all; I'm hungry and just wanted to

take a small bit of your nice pudding, Mistress," cried the stranger.

Right there, the pudding, which was very hot, fell out of his hand, and the bag which held it burst open, strewing the good food in all directions. The woman stopped to save the bag while the stranger and Peter kept on running until they came to the woods. Both were out of breath.

"I'll go home and bring you something to eat," said Peter. "I know my mother'll give it to you."

"Go home, but don't come back. I'll find food, the same as the birds do. A merry good day, Peter, and don't ever lose your dreams."

The stranger went his way, and Peter came home to find his father in great anger, for he had heard the tale of the stolen pudding.

Jacob told the boy sternly he'd have to punish him for keeping company with scamps and thieves. He'd have to teach him so that he would not end on the gallows in Salem some day like a witch—or like a thief.

Poor Peter tried to tell his father the man wasn't a thief, but the more he spoke the more wroth Jacob grew.

Then the mother tried to explain to the angry man that their son did these things because he had a kindly heart. But Jacob said Peter would have to be punished, and punished he was.

Peter wept, but not so much from pain as from bewilderment. He could not understand why his father, whom he loved, would so such a thing. Yet the very next day he waited high on the hill to see him coming home on the horse, golden in the setting sun.

Soon after, Peter was walking along the road and two dogs came by, limping, each with one hind leg tied tight to the body. Such was the law of the town, to keep the dogs from digging for the fish buried in the ground to help the yellow corn grow.

Peter felt sorry for the poor dogs limping along painfully. "It is wrong to tie up the poor animals, and there are many fish in the sea," he said to himself. So he untied them, and they ran off barking joyfully.

But that evening Jacob heard of it, and he called his son a good-for-nothing scalawag who was forever getting into mischief and brought shame to his house.

"It's the second time in a week. He'll come to a bad end," he shouted to the mother, who tried to shield the boy, saying he had untied the dogs because he had a kind heart and was too young to think like older people.

But Jacob didn't listen. He punished Peter just the same.

Again Peter could not understand why his father punished him for doing a kind deed.

The next day Jacob went to Salem to see a witch's hanging, and Peter went to the hill where he always sat to watch his father coming home.

The sunset came in shining glory. All the sky was filled with gold, fiery red, and purple, and the trees and grass, the river, the houses, and the road all had a golden sheen. And now his father came down the road. The sheen covered horse and rider, too, making them blazing bright.

Peter ran up to his father full of love. He had forgotten all about the punishment of the day before.

"Father, father," he cried, "I watched you riding on the road on your golden horse, its mane and tail all silver. It was the most beautiful sight in all the world. When I lie on the grass and look up into the blue sky, and then close my eyes a little, I too ride on a golden horse with a silver mane. I ride over the mountains and over the sea until I come to a magic land."

When Jacob heard this, he turned pale and cried out:

"May God forgive you! You are not speaking the truth! You are bewitched, son, and some day they'll hang you in Salem for it." He dragged Peter home so none would know his shame. Then he ordered him to stay in his room until he would get those devilish notions from his mind.

Poor Peter's heart near broke, for he loved his father dearly and could not understand why he was always angry.

In the night he became ill and spoke of nothing but the golden horse with the silver mane and silver tail. Jacob and his wife sat worried and sad by their son's bedside.

Suddenly Peter cried out:

"Listen, the golden horse is pawing outside. He is calling me!"

Both father and mother rushed out, but all they heard was the pawing of the horse in the stall near by.

Those were the last words Peter spoke. For after that he went where there are many golden horses with silver manes.

The parents grieved and sorrowed, but it did them little good.

So fall came, and one day Jacob rode once again to Salem.

When the sun was setting in a sea of gold, Jacob's wife chanced to be on the hill where Peter had often sat watching for his father's homecoming. She was looking down the valley, and suddenly she saw in the setting sun a horse gleaming golden with a flying silver mane and tail racing down the road. It was Jacob's horse. The horse Peter, her Dream Boy, had always seen! Of which he had always spoken!

Soon the horse came in . . . riderless, its yellow sides beflecked with foam and blood.

There had been a battle with Indians in the woods, and Jacob had been pierced by many arrows and had died.

Now the childless widow knew Peter had been right about the golden horse with the silver mane. She had seen with her own eyes how the flaming sheen of the setting sun had made horse and rider all golden. And she knew for certain that Jacob, her husband, knew it too. For Jacob was with Peter in the land where everything is understood and where beautiful dreams are real. . . .

Jingling Rhymes and Jingling Money

THE story goes there lived in Boston town, in Pudding Lane, a man whose name was Thomas Fleet. That man loved peace and quiet above everything else. Peace he had for a good long time, until he married a comely maid and had many children. Then he had neither peace nor quiet. For Thomas' children, like children in all the world, would make noise: laughing and crying, shouting and playing. That caused Master Thomas great unhappiness.

One day he said to his wife:

"Goodwife, is there no way to end the noisiness of our children so that I can have peace and quiet?"

"Oh, dear husband," she replied, "from morn till night I work hard to keep the house clean and our children well. Yet you complain. You forget such is the way of children since time began. If you would have children in your home, you must have noise as well. But be of good cheer, Thomas, it could be much worse."

That did cheer Thomas a little, though it didn't stop the noise in his home.

It became even worse. For one day little Hope, the youngest daughter, took ill, crying day and night. The doctors came and bled her and gave her pills, but it did little good.

When the doctors didn't help, Mistress Fleet went to see Mother Cary, a kind old woman who tried to help everyone who was sick. But people called her a witch and told all kinds of strange things about her. They said she even went one night over the wild ocean in an egg-shell to a foreign land and back, to pick rosemary by the moonlight for someone who was ill.

When Mistress Fleet came into Mother Cary's little room, she found her with Goody Bess, a friend of hers who loved cats. They were eating beans from a brown bean-pot.

Mistress Fleet greeted Mother Cary and Goody Bess and told them of her woes.

"My little Hope is very ill, and no doctor can cure her. Please, can you help me in my plight? I feel so tired from all the work and worry!"

She looked so thin and worn that both the old women felt very sorry for her.

"I'll give you herbs to cure your little Hope, and I'll give you advice that'll cure your tired look and weak body," said Mother Cary.

She gave her a little of this herb and a little of that and a little of another, telling her to brew a tea for the child. Then she added, "And here's your cure. You work too much with home and children. Why don't you ask your mother, Mistress Goose, to come and help you? She is a widow, all alone, and will be glad to aid you in your labors. Besides, she knows many simples for curing ailments."

Mistress Fleet thanked her, went home, and did exactly as Mother Cary counseled her. She gave the brew to little Hope, and she called her mother to the house. The child was cured, and Mistress Goose came.

All were happy now, save Master Fleet. There was less peace and quiet than ever in that house, for old Mistress Goose had a way of making jingle rhymes to keep the children happy and laughing the whole day long. She would sing:

"There was an old woman who lived in a shoe,
  She had so many children, she didn't know what
      to do."
Or:

  "Mistress Mary, quite contrary,
      How does your garden grow?
  With cockle shells and silver bells,
      And pretty maids all in a row."

The day long she sang the little jingles, and the children sang them with her.

"The King of France went up the hill
    with twenty thousand men;
The King of France came down the hill,
    and never went up again."

And when the children's friends and neighbors came in, they sang the jingles, too. So at all hours there was singing of jingles in the house of Master Fleet, besides the many other noises. Truly it seemed to him like a punishment from on high.

Poor Master Fleet! He'd run far and wide to escape the sound of the singing, jingling rhymes. One day he went to Frog's Pond where stood the ducking stool on which they ducked women who scolded too much. No people were there, and it was quiet.

Soon Mistress Cary and Goody Bess came along followed by nine cats of every size and color.

"Mistress Cary, a pox on you!" said Master Fleet. "Truly you're a witch, for you have brought great unhappiness to me. Why did you ever tell my wife to bring her mother, Mistress Goose, to my house?"

"Would you rather have your wife ill to death from overwork with your many children?" Mother Cary asked testily.

"That's right, Master Fleet," added Goody Bess.

"But what of my misery? How can I stop her mother, Mistress Goose, from always singing jingling rhymes? All my children sing them day and night with her. And so do all the children in the neighborhood. The noise is worse than Indians' war whoops."

"You can't stop Mistress Goose from making her jingling rhymes, nor the children from singing them, Master Fleet, nor should you, for it makes the day bright and happy for all of 'em. But, since I've given your goodwife advice that helped her, I'll now give you some as well, which'll help you, too. Maybe you'll sing a different tune, a bright jingling tune," and she laughed.

"And what advice is that, Mother Cary?" asked Master Fleet.

"Why don't you put these jingling rhymes of Mother Goose to your own benefit? Certain, if your children love them, and the children of your neighbors, too, the children of all Boston town will love them. For this reason why don't you print them so that other grandmothers will sing them to their grandchildren, even as does Grandmother Goose to yours? It should bring you good money, that is certain."

Now Master Fleet loved money as well as any man and maybe a little more. So he took Mother Cary's good advice even as his goodwife had done. He printed Mother Goose's jingles, each and every one, beginning with:

"Tom, Tom, the piper's son,
    Stole a pig and away he run.
  The pig was eat, and Tom was beat,
    And Tom went roaring down the street."

He sold them to all and everyone. Soon every child in every home in Boston town and thereabouts was singing the little jingles good Grandma Goose sang to her own grandchildren.

Do you think Master Fleet minded the noise now?— never one little, little bit. He too sang Mother Goose's jingling rhymes—especially the one he liked best:

"I love sixpence, pretty little sixpence.
I love sixpence better than my life."

Magic in Marblehead

IN Marblehead, where the great sea and the strong fishermen are forever battling, there was, many years ago, a young fellow who wasn't so very bad and who wasn't so very good, either. Most of the time he was more bad than good. One time he was put in the stocks and another time they cut his hair round like a pumpkin. The good minister tried his best to make of him a goodly fellow, but he failed sadly.

One wild night when the rumbling marsh-lion was roaring in the woods, Jonathan, that was his name, went to the tavern with some companions. He stayed there until the tavern keeper turned the lantern down and closed the door and said it was time to go home.

Each went his own way quickly, for a storm was coming in the starry sky, and soon the night was black as Egypt. A wind rushed up from the sea fit to smash a full-manned boat, but Jonathan never noted it. He was warm and opened his doublet wide.

Suddenly the sea and the coast rang with a great cry,

"Save me! Save me!" That was the English lady pleading for mercy of the pirates. Though she had been dead for years her cries were often heard on stormy nights.

But Jonathan did not mind this, either. His legs just kept on walking, and he did not try to stop them. So he went along the crooked streets of Marblehead, going in and out and out and in, while the winds whistled wildly all around. All of a sudden, he did not know how or from where, there stood before him a gray-haired old hag dressed in ragged skirt and torn shawl and a string of wolves' teeth around her neck.

"There you are, Jonathan. I've been looking for you for a long time. Now I've found you, and a fine night it is for our meeting," the old woman screeched through the howling wind.

"Looking for me!" Jonathan said in great surprise. "And who are you, dame?"

"I'm Mammy Red of Marblehead. You and I are much alike, and I'd like you to do me a little favor. I want you to go to Widow Prudence and take away the wood she gathered for the freezing winter months and keep it for yourself. That will save you gathering yours, and put her in fine misery for the want of it on icy days."

"Now that's a seemly deed, Mammy Red," cried Jonathan, all aglee. "It will save me cutting the wood and will make the widow freeze. A goodly thought indeed."

"And, if you do as I tell you, you can come this night

to the witches' feast, where there'll be dancing and carousing with our grand Black Master himself present."

"I'll come," cried Jonathan, "but first I'll go to Widow Prudence and take the wood from her."

"When you're done, meet me at the edge of the town. I'll wait there for you," said Mammy Red of Marblehead, as she vanished with the howling wind.

So Jonathan turned into one crooked lane, and then into another and another, coming nearer and nearer to Widow Prudence's house. The nearer he came the slower he walked. Maybe it was the wind holding him back, or maybe it was the better part of him doing it. Then he stopped altogether. That better part of him had come up very strong. He thought the hard work of gathering fresh wood would be too much for the old widow. Perhaps it was better not to steal it.

Suddenly he heard the beating of horses' hoofs louder than hail on the rocks. There, coming toward him, was a carriage drawn by four fiery horses. From their hoofs flew sizzling sparks, and from their nostrils came smoky sulphur you could smell afar. In the carriage sat a tall man with two little horns on his head and two green fiery eyes below his forehead. In his hand was a snake with a wriggly gleaming head which he used as a whip. It was the Devil himself, and you couldn't mistake him for anyone else.

"So you think you can escape me, Jonathan," the Devil shouted with a voice that was a scream and a roar at one and the same time. "You've gone too far, brother; you belong to me and can't go back. Take those logs, then come to the meeting."

The snake-whip snapped lightning streaks, the horses' hoofs struck sizzling sparks, and it smelled sulpur all around.

Jonathan was frightened as he had never been before. He ran and stumbled along, the wild rider and his horses after him. And all the time he heard the howling voice: "Do your deed and then come to meet Mammy Red."

Jonathan was now at Widow Prudence's little house. It was silent and peaceful as if no evil could touch it. But Jonathan never noted that. He just picked up the logs that lay on the side of the house, the pine, the hemlock, birch, and maple logs which the poor old woman had brought together for the cold winter.

Never before did he work so fast at an evil deed. You'd think the Devil himself gave strength to his arms and wings to his feet.

When it was all done he turned his steps in the direction where Mammy Red said she'd meet him.

First he walked swiftly and the wind blew fiercely; then he walked slower and it began raining; then he walked still slower and there was a low rumbling thunder.

He walked slowly because the better part of him was coming up strong. "What if I don't go to the meeting with Mammy Red? I don't have to," he thought to himself. Right then he came past Ol' Dimond's house, Ol' Dimond, the kind wizard of Marblehead. It was a little

house with old-fashioned flowers all around. At that minute the good part of Jonathan was very strong.

"Here's one who can help," he cried, for now he didn't want to see Mammy Red or go to any meeting.

He pounded at the wizard's door, and out came Cato, his old black servant.

"What you want this time o' the night?" he asked crossly.

"I want to speak to Ol' Dimond, and I want to speak to him quickly. He must save me."

"Ol' Massa Dimond, he went to the burial ground by the sea to save a ship an' crew that can't come in from the wild ocean. You go an' fin' him there."

It stormed great guns, but Jonathan ran swiftly.

At the burial ground he found Ol' Dimond in his big greatcoat standing among the white burial stones. He was waving his arms wildly in the flying wind, shouting orders that could be heard above the roaring, above the thunder, above everything. He shouted so loud a captain in a floundering ship out in the sea heard him so clear he steered his way safely toward Marblehead.

Jonathan cried:

"Ol' Dimond, I met Mammy Red of Marblehead and she told me to steal the wood Widow Prudence gathered for the winter months. I did, and now I must go to the Devil's meeting. But I don't want to go to the meeting at all for they'll make me sell my soul. Help me, Ol' Dimond, so I don't have to go and lose my soul."

Ol' Dimond the wizard screamed his orders to the

floundering ship at sea while listening with one ear to Jonathan. Then he shouted at him:

"Go back and return the logs you stole from Widow Prudence. The Evil One and Mammy Red of Marblehead can never touch you while you are doing a kind deed. They have power over you only when you do evil. Go, and with the help of Providence you'll be saved."

Jonathan ran as fast as his legs would go and once again began to drag the logs, but this time it was from his house to the widow's house.

The wet rain trickled down his face, and his breath came short in the stormy night, but doing a kindly deed and fear of the Evil One gave strength to his arms and wings to his feet.

Mammy Red of Marblehead screamed curses you could hear as far as Gloucester and Boston town when she saw what Jonathan was doing. The Devil raced wildly through the narrow streets, his steeds pouring fiery sparks from their hoofs and yellow sulphur from their nostrils. But Jonathan kept on dragging the logs until all were back at the widow's house.

When the Evil One and Mammy Red saw they could not stop Jonathan they gave up and said they'd try another time. But there was no other time, for Jonathan had learned a good lesson that night from Ol' Dimond, the good wizard. From then on he was never bad at all.

The Lord of Massachusetts

DOWN in Newburyport by the sea, in Massachusetts, lived Lord Timothy Dexter. No lord ever made by a king or queen was better than this lord made by himself. And wasn't he proud of it!

But the people of Newburyport were forever making fun of him. They made fun of him because he had a funny little yellow dog with a curly tail like a pig, and they made fun of him because of the strange things he'd trade in foreign lands.

One time he filled two ships with cats and sent them to a hot country. The wharves in the hot country were full of large, gray rats, and there were not enough cats to hurt a mouse. So the people there gladly bought the cats at a fancy price, and Lord Dexter made much silver.

One day some rich merchants of the town thought they'd play a joke on Lord Dexter. They wanted to make him do something silly, whereby he would lose his money. For not a few of them were jealous of his luck and his wealth.

147

They met him by the gate of his garden, those rich
merchants, and told him that the people of the West
Indies were greatly in want of warming pans with long
handles, such as were used in those days in New England.

Of course, you all know it is very hot in the West
Indies, and people never, never use warming pans in
their beds. Why, they are too hot there even to wear
clothes. But the merchants thought Lord Dexter was the
greatest of all fools and would take their silly advice. He
promised to do it, and they went off happy, telling one
another that silly Dexter would surely lose a good deal
of his money this time.

Now, it so happened, a poor brother and sister, Hester and Joshua by name, overheard the merchants tell
how Lord Dexter was a fool and would lose his good
money. Straightaway they ran to Lord Dexter's mansion
to tell him the tale.

The merchant was sitting in the large square chamber
of his big square house, his private poet, Jonathan Plummer, on one side, and Madame Hopper, who had a
double set of teeth and could tell fortunes, on the other.

Hester and Joshua told Lord Dexter what the merchantmen had said—that they were sending Lord Dexter
on a fool's errand where he was sure to lose his money.

"On a fool's errand they would send me, and a rich
ending it will have," roared Lord Dexter. "Three nights
I have dreamt of warming pans and what they would do

in the West Indies. Perhaps Providence tells me to do it through these dishonest merchants."

"Perhaps that's the truth," said Madame Hopper, who had a hen for a 'familiar.'

> "Lord Dexter is a man of fame,
> Most celebrated is his name,"

sang Jonathan Plummer, Lord Dexter's private poet.

"The West Indies are so hot that people only wear loincloths. That's what I learned in school," said Hester.

"The West Indies are very hot, sugar cane grows there, and they melt the cane over fires to get the sweet sugar. That's what I learned in school," said Joshua, Hester's brother.

"Did you say they melt the sugar over fires in the West Indies?" cried Lord Timothy Dexter in his deep, bass voice.

"That they do indeed, and it is so hot they never wear shoes or coats. Why should they need warming pans?"

"Maybe they do, and maybe they don't," roared Lord Dexter lustily, "but I have an idea. An idea fit for me, Lord Dexter, first lord of America and first in the East, first in the West, and greatest philosopher in the Western World."

"That's written in the stars," said Madame Hopper, who told fortunes under the yellow moon.

> "Lord Dexter like King Solomon,
> Hath gold and silver by the ton,"

said Jonathan Plummer, the fishmonger poet.

"And now I'll make more silver and gold, thanks to Hester and Joshua and the Newburyport merchants who'd make a fool of me," said the merchantman.

Then Lord Dexter sent men to buy warming pans the country round. He sent them to Boston on the bay, and he sent them to Plymouth by the sea; he sent them to Salem, the famous witch-hunting town, and he sent them to New York, the gay city of the East. When he had got together forty-two thousand bright and shiny warming pans with long handles both plain and fancy, he loaded them on nine ships and whispered in secret to the captains what they had to do. He told them to keep it a tight secret so none would get ahead in the venture.

The ships sailed the high ocean when the sun shone golden on the dancing water and when the moon shone silvery on the silent sea, until they reached the rich West Indies.

There the people gathered around the ships, and the captains showed their wares. They told them they could use the warming pans with long handles to boil the sugar, instead of the round pots with short stubby handles on which they were always burning their hands. Before three days were over the warming pans were sold to the very last one.

Again the ships went sailing high when the sun shone golden on the dancing water and when the moon shone silvery on the silent sea until they reached Newburyport town.

On the wharf waited Lord Timothy Dexter, Jonathan Plummer the fishmonger poet, Madame Hopper the witch lady, Hester, Joshua, and many, many, merchantmen.

"Lord Timothy Dexter," cried the captain of the "Mehitabel," the largest of all the ships, "you'll be richer now than ever you were, for we've sold every one of those warming pans just as you ordered us to do."

"Huzza!" cried Lord Dexter.

"It was written in the stars," said Madame Hopper.

"Lord Dexter like King Solomon,
    Hath gold and silver by the ton,"

cried Jonathan Plummer, the fishmonger poet.

"Fool's luck, fool's luck," cried the merchantmen of Newburyport by the sea.

"No fool's luck at all," said the first lord of America. "No fool's luck, but shrewd man's wisdom. I'll tell you something you didn't know. You thought you'd make a fool of me and send me on a fool's errand so I'd lose my gold and silver. But Heaven watched over me and sent me these two children, Hester and Joshua, who told me what they learned in school. They told me that in the West Indies people heat the sugar cane to get the sugar out of it. Now a wise man puts learning to proper use. What could be finer than warming pans with long handles for melting sweet sugar cane? So, I bought forty-two thousand of 'em and sent them out on my ship. They've just returned and brought me seventy-nine per cent profit, and Hester and Joshua will get their proper share.

"Ha! gentlemen! Remember, the next time put your learning to proper use even as I did—I, Lord Dexter, the first lord in these United States, and the greatest philosopher in the Western World."

> "Lord Dexter is a man of fame,
> Most celebrated is his name;
> More precious far than gold that's pure
> Lord Dexter shines forever more,"

> Said Jonathan Plummer clear and hale.
> I say the same; here ends my tale.

The Devil in the Steeple

THIS happened when no place in all America was so much troubled by the Evil One as the State of Massachusetts, the state of the Pilgrim Fathers. Truly there was no city or hamlet there that didn't have some kind of trouble with the Devil.

Now at that time there were three brothers in Ipswich town—Ebenezer, Josiah, and Jacob—who loved a merry trick more than squirrels love nuts. One was a drummer, the other a horn blower, and the third sang like a robin. They never missed a chance for jest or jollity.

One day they decided to teach a fellow, Mark Quitter by name, to stop drinking and carousing. So they took a young calf and dropped it slowly down the wide black chimney of Mark's house. When the black beast landed with its four cloven hoofs on the fireplace, Mark was frightened clear to Jerusalem. He ran to the selectmen of the town and complained bitterly and asked that the brothers be punished for their misdeed. The selectmen didn't think long and gave their judgment on the spot. They said:

"Ebenezer, Josiah, and Jacob, you must do double free work on the church steeple we are building high on the hill, where the great man of God will preach. The holy man has come from across the sea and across the land, many, many miles, to pour good words into the hearts of men."

Up they went, the three, Ebenezer, Josiah, and Jacob, up they went to work, singing, for they loved to labor for the Lord, high up overlooking the green river and the wide sea. The hammers clanged, the nails went deep, and the slender steeple rose in the widespread wind.

Suddenly, just when the sun stood in the middle of the sky, and the three brothers were eating bread and fruit, Ebenezer cried out:

"Behold! Josiah and Jacob. Look! Quick! right behind the scaffolding!"

Josiah and Jacob looked, and there they saw a sight that filled them full of fear and made their eyes come near out of their heads. But soon the fear was gone. Cried Josiah:

"It's the Devil for certain."

And Jacob added, "It's not mouse nor man, nor big-tailed rat, but it's the Devil himself with horns on his head."

There, in very truth, the Devil did sit on the beam of the wooden scaffold: horns on his head, and a long black tail ending in a brush of hair just like a cow's.

"Get hence! Evil One! in the name of the Lord!" Ebenezer cried loudly.

"In the Lord's name, away," Josiah said.

" 'Tis the house of God!" Jacob added.

But the Devil sat there moving neither foot nor brow, just grinning and never paying heed. That made the three merry brothers good and angry.

"Away from here!" Ebenezer cried, and his voice was sharp as a knife.

"I'm here to stay, and you can do me no harm," the Devil replied in a friendly-like, squeaky voice.

"You are there for mischief, I know, and for torment-ing the innocent. Run away quickly, or else I'll send you flying far out in the sea," spoke Josiah, and there was thunder in his voice.

"There'll be no biting, pricking, pinching, neck-twist-ing, nor calamities to the cattle in our town. We'll see to that," Jacob added, growling like a bear.

But the Devil sat there never moving, just flipping his tail playfully right and left like a friendly dog. Never-theless, the three brothers knew the Devil was up to some mischief even though he was grinning pleasantly.

"You go!" Ebenezer cried, getting up from where he sat.

"I'll not go at all. I'll stay here and find pleasure in my own way. You can't drive me away," the Devil said defiantly.

"We can't!" They shouted together so loud that the steeple swayed from side to side. Then the three rushed around the scaffold where the Devil sat and booted him with their cowhide boots all at the same time.

Never was there such booting before. It hit the Fiend with the force of thunder. He flew down the steeple into the rock below, and he hit that stone so hard you can see the mark of the cloven foot there to this very day.

No sooner did he hit the rock than he bounced right back into the steeple, but try as the three merry brothers would, they could not find him.

So they went to the great preacher, who stayed in a farmer's house near by, and told him what had happened.

"Never fear," the preacher said. "I'll find the Devil, and once I find him he'll never bother you again."

The three brothers went merrily back to their work.

But as for the Devil, he was hiding behind a pile of boards, muttering angry words and swearing he'd still have his way and would make mischief or lead some good person from the path of virtue.

The next day the preacher came to preach the word of God. There was a great crowd of people listening to him. His sermon was sweeter than honey and brought balm to the good and fear to the sinful.

While he was in the midst of explaining how the good sit on the right hand of God, he suddenly spied the Devil high on the ridgepole of the steeple. There he stood with folded arms, his tail switching from side to side, watching for some man or woman he could lead into mischief.

Then the great preacher raised his voice in praise of God as he had never done before. He shouted in the wind that only the word of the Lord would save the world. He roared so angrily against those who did not obey the commandments that the building shook in its foundation. There never was heard such voice of thunder of holy words. It was mightier than the roaring of the wind and the shouting of a tempest. It was so mighty it hit the Devil and raised him from the steeple like a feather and flung him far, far away. The force of the sound and the holy words of the great preacher flung him so far away, and put such fear into him, he never came that way again.

The three merry brothers, Ebenezer, Josiah, and Jacob, and all the others seeing this, shouted the praises of God and lived a goodly life.

And from that day the people of Ipswich were never troubled by the Evil One like the rest of Massachusetts.

A Merry Tale of Merrymount

THIS is a merry tale of merry men right in New England.

Many years ago there was a town called Merrymount, where every man, woman, and child was merry, as merry as could be, playing and dancing whenever they had a minute free.

Amongst this merry company were Ralph and Ruth, two young people in the springtime of life who were in love with each other. When they walked hand in hand in the greening woods or along the flowing river, Ralph'd say, "I'll soon build us a house, and we'll wed, never to be parted."

And Ruth just squeezed Ralph's hand and said nothing but smiled happily, which was a language Ralph well understood.

When Master Morton, who was the most important man in all the settlement, saw them, he would say these two, Ruth and Ralph, were just the right kind of people for Merrymount and should soon be married.

One day Master Morton was in the woods and caught a young bear. Ralph taught the beast to dance and play the pipe, and, when the other settlers saw the bear so dancing, they joined in the jolly game. And, since it was the harvest time of the year, they held a great feast and played sham battles, blindman's buff, and other kinds of gay pastimes.

Then they made an Indian image of corn sheaves and brown autumn foliage and built a great bonfire, dancing around it with glee and joy. Ralph and Ruth were in the fore of all the jollities.

But the stern Pilgrim fathers, who lived all around them, did not like this gaiety and warned them that, if they wouldn't stop, woe would soon befall them.

When Yuletide came to Merrymount, the people there crowned a gay fellow King Christmas and made it a holiday of singing, dancing, and feasting—altogether a celebration such as had never been in our land before. Then and there it was decided that Ralph and Ruth would marry the coming Maytime, which is the right and proper time for marriage.

When the Pilgrims and the Governor heard of the Christmas jollities they sent a message to the colony and warned them to cease such godless doings or they'd be punished for it—and that it was the last warning.

The people of Merrymount never heeded the stern message. They went about their way being happy and living their merry lives even though the Pilgrim fathers looked with black anger at these carryings-on.

Thus Maytime came, when birds and flowers and trees and greens join in grand springtime life. So did the people of Merrymount, most of all Ralph and Ruth, for their wedding day was nearing.

Master Morton ordered a goodly pine full eighty feet in height to be cut, and Ralph and the other young fellows fell to work with a right good will. Then they nailed a pair of buck's horns near the top and set the pole in the ground.

Came the marriage day for Ruth and Ralph, which was part of the May-day celebration.

Early in the morning the young people, Ruth and Ralph amongst them, gathered blossoms and peeled birch bark and made flying banners. They bedecked the Maypole forthwith so that it looked gay as a dancer in festive clothes.

Then all the people of Merrymount and many Indians from the neighboring woods came and feasted and danced. Ralph and Ruth were chosen King and Queen of the May.

All the day long the jollities never ceased. When the sun was setting, they put masks on their faces and garlands on their heads, built a great fire, and danced and sang around the Maypole.

So the wedding hour came for Ralph and Ruth. They stood in the center, and the clergyman stood ready to say the holy words. But right then there burst upon them a band of Pilgrims with guns and staves, who ordered all the jollities ended.

There were many Pilgrims, and they were armed, while the people of Merrymount were there for pleasure only. What could they do but obey the cruel order?

The Governor chopped the pole down with his sword. Masks and garlands were torn off. All were ordered to depart, and all obeyed save Ralph and Ruth, who stood there in anger and sadness, seeing their wedding come to nought.

Said the Governor sternly:

"You two were King and Queen of these ribald carryings-on, and will receive hard punishment for it."

"If I were stronger and had as many men as you, I'd punish you for breaking up my wedding day," Ralph answered bravely. "There's no harm in our merrymaking."

The Governor looked at the fearless face, all aglow with courage and anger, and felt a little ashamed for what he had done. But he did not show it in his countenance.

"So you two were to be married," said he. " 'Tis not too late for the ceremony, I think. But first," and his voice was hard and cold, "both of you take off your pagan crowns and garlands and look like God-fearing Christians."

Both did this slowly.

"Now," said the Governor, "you, Ralph, will be punished for your misdeeds. Your hair will be cut round-fashioned this very instant, and as for you, Ruth. . . ."

Spoke Ralph quickly, "I'll take her punishment, too."

"Do you want it so?" the Governor asked the girl.

"No," said Ruth. "I'll take my own punishment and his as well."

The Governor was silent for a time. Then he said, "Take Ralph and carry out my orders. Then bring him back at once."

It was done quickly, and Ralph came back to where Ruth was standing.

"Now you two'll be married according to our holy laws, and I hope you'll live a Christian life without these ungodly shameful deeds," he said with a stern face and kindly eye.

They were married, and so the day ended happily for Ralph and Ruth, but not for Merrymount.

The stern Governor drove Master Morton from the land, and the merry town of Merrymount soon was no more. But the people from this happy place went among the stern Pilgrim Fathers and tried to teach them that merrymaking was good in the eyes of God as it was in their lives.

The Sacred Cod
and the Striped Haddock

WHEN the sharp silver moon marches along the road of stars over Nantucket and all the Cape, the fathers are out on the sea fishing for cod and haddock. When the bright, warm fire blazes in the little white clapboard homes along the coasts, and there is time before bed, mothers'll tell stories—fishermen's stories fit for young 'uns who live around the Cape. This is one of the stories they tell.

"When the good Lord Jesus still walked on the earth and spoke to people, He took a journey on a ship. After three days the ship anchored, and He and His disciples went on land into a desert. The people who lived on the coast heard it and came from everywhere by the thousands to follow Him. They listened to His golden words which were like a drink of cold, fresh water on a hot day.

"All day the Lord walked, followed by the people, and in the evening they came to a place where there were only shrubs and grass and not much of that.

"The good Lord sat down, His disciples sat around Him, and the people stood in rows deep.

"Said Andrew, the disciple, who was Peter's brother:

" 'This is a desert place, Lord, and there is no bread or meat for all these people. They are tired and hungry from walking. We have but five loaves of bread and two fish, a cod and a haddock, in our basket. Though the fish are large and the breads are big they are not enough to feed all who followed you. Lord, tell them to go to the village to buy food to eat.'

"But the Lord Jesus answered:

" 'I do not send away the hungry. Let them come and sit around me.'

"So all the people came and sat around Jesus. And He took the baskets with the loaves and fishes and blessed them. Then He took out the loaves and gave them to the disciples to give to the people. And the more He took out the more came out—there were enough loaves to feed everyone there. Then He took out the cod with His forefinger and His thumb and gave it to Peter, who was a fisherman, to give to the people. To this very day you can see marks on codfish where the Lord Jesus touched the fish. And the cod multiplied without end for all to eat.

"Now you know, the Devil is always fishing round the world for mischief and trouble and is terribly jealous of Jesus. He often follows in the Lord's footsteps to see if he can't undo His good deeds. That day he followed Him right among the disciples, and when he saw the miracle that Jesus did with the loaves of bread and the cod, he said to himself kind o' boasting:

" 'I can do what Jesus does.'

"So when no one was looking he slyly took the other fish, the haddock, out of the basket to increase it a thousandfold just as the Lord had done with the cod.

"But his fingers were burning with brimstone, and the haddock knew at once it was in the hands of the Devil. It wriggled and squirmed and slithered as quick as it could through the burning hot fingers until it fell to the ground—and there were two long, burnt, black marks on the side of the haddock, which have remained there to this day.

"The good Lord picked up the fish from the ground and blessed it and gave it to Peter to give to the people, and the haddock multiplied just the same as the cod. There was enough for all the thousand who were there to eat, so they were not hungry.

"That is how you can tell the difference between the sacred cod which the Lord touched and the burnt haddock which Satan touched."

This is a tale boys and girls hear when their fathers are out fishing on the sea and there is a little time before bedtime.

And when the fathers come home with full boats, they rush to the beach to see if the fish are sacred cod touched by the fingers of the Lord, or haddock burnt by Satan's hot fingers.

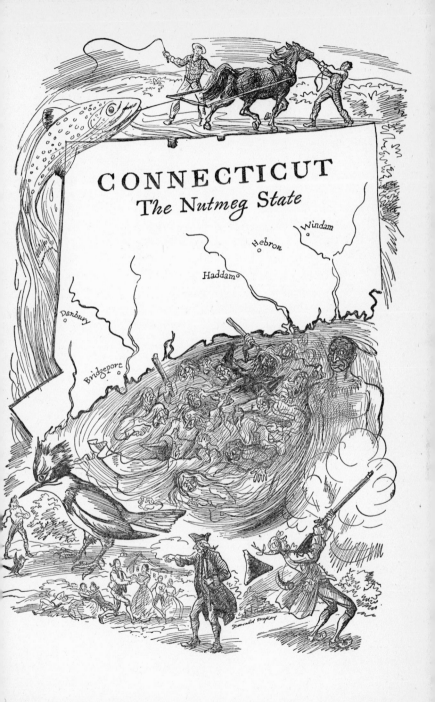

CONNECTICUT
The Nutmeg State

Windam

Hebron

Haddam

Danbury

Bridgeport

Donald McKay

Tiny Perry

YEARS ago, there was a tiny store in the Big Basin in Connecticut. In that tiny store lived a tiny man selling good things for tiny money. Tiny Perry was his name, and though he was small in size he was a giant in goodness to everyone, but most of all to children and to animals. Never would a child pass through his door but he would give it a gift; never would an animal seek shelter in his home and not find it.

One day Tiny Perry heard a tinkling at the tiny gate covered with pink petunias and candytufts. Quick footsteps came along the path, past the iron pot filled with bright yellow and blue moss roses. Then the little bell rang at the door, and in rushed little James, all out of breath and wet from running.

He didn't look at the wall pictures of the Indians and the General as he always did, and he didn't look at the drawers for candy or toys. He just walked up to Tiny Perry, who sat behind the counter, and said:

"I ran away from home."

Tiny Perry shook his shaggy head and looked with his soft brown eyes at the boy for a time. Then he spoke softly.

"Why did ye run away?"

"Because father sold a gun and shells to a man to kill a baby fawn. He brought it to the house dead and bleedin'. I ran away so I wouldn't look at it."

"No man should kill God's critters just fer sport. Ye've a kind heart, little James."

"You must do something about it, Mister Perry."

" 'Deed I will. It's not right. Now here's somethin' fer ye."

He opened a tiny drawer in his counter and took out a stick of red and white candy and gave it to the hot-faced boy.

"Now get ye home like a good little fellow, and I'll pray to the Lord to stop people from killin' His poor critters wantonly."

The boy went home feeling better, but as for Tiny Perry he thought with all his might what could be done to stop big men from killing animals for no reason at all.

In the evening he sat down near the sweet-smelling candytufts, looked at Green Pond Mountain, and played on his flute a sweet song in the silvery moonlight. It sounded like a fairy wind running in the soft grass or maybe a song played by the stars on high. And, while he played, there came from the blue night air the girl he loved who had gone from him long, long ago.

She bent down and whispered in his ear, and Tiny Perry smiled happily.

The next morning, when he rose, the smile was still there. He closed the gate of his tiny store and went to town, a basket on his arm.

He had walked only a little way when there ran up to him a fat, round raccoon that rubbed its long sharp muzzle and small round ear against his boots, moving its white-ringed tail slowly from side to side friendly like.

"God gave us a fine day, little fellow. You an' I are pretty near the same in size, aren't we, long-nose? an' we understand God, don't we?" spoke Tiny Perry.

He laughed aloud joyfully, stroked the raccoon's fur, and then made a funny little sound just like a wood-chuck that's eating young cabbage.

The fat raccoon scampered around and answered:

"Tiny Perry, why do you go to town so early in the morning?"

"I'm goin' to town so early in the mornin' 'cause I must buy red an' white candy fer little boys, tea fer nice ladies, an' I must do somethin'll stop hunters from shootin' innocent animals."

"Nobody shoots me."

"That's on account of ye're friends with everybody in town. But all yer brothers in the woods, jest as fine as ye, have no such luck. Now I got to arrange it so hunters won't shoot the critters in the woods jest as they don't shoot ye."

The raccoon ran in all directions excitedly at these words.

"Tiny Perry, if you can do this you'll be loved by all the animals more . . . more . . . more than eating!" cried the little rolypoly.

"Let's both think about how to do it."

The two walked along the green road in the shining sun thinking hard about how to stop shooting animals just for fun. They came to the turn in the road and saw the white steeple of the church.

The ring-tailed raccoon suddenly leaped high in the air and cried:

"Sit down, Tiny Perry. I'll tell you how to stop the hunters' killing."

The two sat down on the soft grass, and the birds sang sweetly all around them.

"I know how you can stop the hunters from shooting animals for fun."

"How?" asked Tiny Perry.

"Why not shoot the guns they carry instead of shooting animals?" said the raccoon.

"That's fine; how can we do that?" cried Tiny Perry. And in the same breath he shouted, "I know! I know!"

He got up quickly and began running toward the town, the raccoon running all around him.

Tiny Perry went right into the big store where they sold candy, flour, nails, shoes, guns, shooting powder, and many more things besides. First he bought what he needed—striped candy and green tea, sugar and needles, bread and beans. Then he said to the store man:

"Store man, make me the strongest shootin' shells ye ever made. Make 'em strong enough to shoot the biggest animal that ever was—even strong enough to shoot the gun apart that shoots the shells."

The store man knew Tiny Perry and liked him well, so he made the strongest shooting shells he'd ever made and put them into nice blue wrappers.

"They're strong enough fer to shoot a great big bear; even strong enough fer to shoot a great big moose, an' it needs a mighty powerful gun to shoot 'em, Tiny Perry," said he.

Tiny Perry came out of the store whistling a little tune, and there were James and two more boys and a girl petting the ring-tailed raccoon. When they saw the little man with the shaggy hair and the brown eyes they ran to him.

Said James in a whisper:

"Tiny Perry, have you found a way to stop killing animals?"

Then they all crowded close around him.

"That I have indeed, little animals an' big 'uns."

He went off whistling a funny tune, and the raccoon followed him, running up and down and all around, gaily, as if he had eaten the finest cabbage that ever was.

They came to the tiny gate, and there the ring-tailed raccoon said a happy good-by, for both knew well that from then on there'd be mighty little animal shooting in the Big Basin and round about.

Do you know why?

Why, every time hunters came to Tiny Perry's shop to buy gun shells to shoot animals, he sold them the shells in the bright blue wrappers. When the hunters used them, BANG! the guns would kick so hard or maybe burst altogether, and there was such a terrible, loud noise and so much smoke, the whole countryside was warned, and all the animals hid where no hunter could find them.

Then little James and all the boys and girls who hated to see animals killed were happy. But the happiest of all was Tiny Perry, sitting at his tiny door by the sweet-smelling flowers, playing his flute to the moon and the stars until his love would come to him. Sometimes the fat raccoon and other animals joined him, and then they'd all dance to the playing without fear of being shot by hunters—all thanks to Tiny Perry's shells with the shiny blue wrappers round them.

The Smart Husband
and the Smarter Wife

ONCE there lived in Cowplain in Connecticut a God-fearing fellow named Josiah, who was rich in goods of the world. He had a fine house and he had fat cows; he had a strong horse and much money; but best of all he had a good head on his shoulders and could think out things proper.

One Sunday after church he was sitting in his high-backed chair by the fireside thinking about this and that, when a thought he'd never had before came to his mind. Spoke he to himself as was ever his wont:

"I've all man kin desire, and I'm greatly blessed and happy indeed. I'm so happy, I'm afeared when my time comes fer me to go to Heaven in a chariot I'll be loath to leave. Nay, I know for certain I'll be unhappy. An' I don't wish to be unhappy ever. I must do somethin' 'bout this."

Thereupon he thought again for a long time and spoke again to himself:

"Now, here is a good thought. Perhaps if I had some honest trouble in life jest as my neighbors, I'd be glad to go to Heaven instead of bein' sorry."

Then he thought again for a long time and spoke again to himself:

"When I meet my friends in the tavern they all speak more 'bout the trouble they have wi' wives than any trouble ever with their horses or cows. It'd seem to me if I got me a wife I'd have troubles, too, so when my time comes to go to Heaven I'll be pretty glad to do so. And since I'm the most contented man in Cowplain near Cedar Mountain, I must get me the worst wife to make certain I'll have plenty o' trouble."

The next morning he set out and traveled up and down the roads of Connecticut to find him the worst wife he could find. He also looked in on Cabul Hill, Hang Dog, and Vexation Hill. Though he looked everywhere, he couldn't find the right kind of wife he sought. So he turned home again.

When he came to the first meadow and passed by Andrus' house, his nearest neighbor, he heard a screaming and screeching to split the ears. That was Hannah, Andrus' only daughter, whom none would marry, for she was the crossest creature in all the state. She'd argue, and nip and nag friends and neighbors, just for the sake of arguing, nipping, and nagging. Truth to tell, she was the worst woman in all the land.

"Thanks unto the Lord! That's the wife for me," Josiah cried joyfully. "And she was right near by all the time while I was a-lookin' for her all over the land."

He rode quickly right up to the door and knocked loudly. But they heard him not for the scolding and screaming. So he knocked harder, and the door flung wide open. Hannah stood there, with brown-red hair flying in all directions like frightened sparrows, and eyes blazing paths of dark lightning.

"An' what brings you here?" she cried angrily.

"It's the Lord's will that ye marry me, Hannah," said Josiah.

Hannah caught her breath quicker than a jack rabbit running and pinched herself sideways to make sure she wasn't dreaming. No man had ever spoken such words to her before, let alone one so rich as Josiah. Then her answer jumped out of her mouth:

"The Lord's will be done, Josiah."

So the two were wedded, and things went well indeed. Hannah made plenty of trouble, and it looked as if Josiah would gladly go any time to Heaven without feeling sorry to leave.

One evening he was sitting on a bench with Sled and Hunn, his two best friends, and some other men, in front of the green, and one queried him how he fared with Hannah.

Said Josiah, "Faith, it couldn't be better. She scolds the day long, never givin' me no peace. It's just what I want her to do."

"Now that is a strange thing for a husband to want," said Sled.

"I'd like to know why ye married the worst shrew that ever was?" asked Hunn.

"I'll tell ye why, friend Hunn," spoke Josiah. "I had every joy a man kin want on this earth, and I was afeared when my time came to go to Heaven in a chariot I'd be sorry to leave Cowplain. So I figured I'd be less sorry if I had some trouble just like you and all the others have. Now I've got plenty o' trouble. I couldn't find a worse wife in all our great big land, yet I'm not complaining, the contrary, I am pleased."

Hunn and Sled and all the others listened, ears big as elephants', and, since Hunn was a great gossip, it wasn't long before all Cowplain knew the tale—and Hannah heard it, too.

She was sitting with some womenfolk in her home roasting apples, busy at stitching a long sampler and talking gossip while the menfolk were at the tavern talking politics.

Said Abigail, who had been Hannah's friend for years:

"I never did expect such a thing from Josiah, though I knew he wasn't silly love-cracked. Know you what he said? He said he had married you so you'd make his life so miserable he'd gladly go to Heaven in a chariot when his time came round. He said if life on earth were too pleasurable and without trouble he'd never want to leave it."

"Josiah said 'twas the Lord's will that I marry him," cried Hannah stoutly.

"So he said," spoke another. "So he said, but it had a different meaning from what you thought. He didn't tell you all. But he told it to my husband Hunn. He said that he married you so you'd bring him trouble and he'd be mighty glad indeed to leave this earth."

Hannah was madder than a cat tied in a sack. She fumed and raved, ranted and screamed, telling all the womenfolk what she'd do to her husband when he came home that night.

All of a sudden she ceased her ranting and stood silent for a long time. A smile came slowly to her face, such as was never there before since the day she was born. Her smile grew bigger and bigger, and all the women looked at her in great surprise.

"Good friends," she cried pleasantly, "I'll cheat my husband in his hopes. I'll be no packhorse to carry him to Heaven. You just wait and see!" Then she laughed most pleasantly, a thing she'd never done before.

When Josiah came home that night he wasn't certain he'd come to the right place. Instead of scolding and crying, Hannah greeted him with a loud kiss. Morever, she was kind and good as she'd never been. And her goodness and kindness never ceased.

From that day on Josiah had the finest wife in all the land, and that put the poor man to great worries. 'Twas not what he'd bargained for. It gave him no peace of mind, and for days and days he thought on't.

Then one day, while he was walking behind his oxen, digging a furrow in the ground, a truly good thought came to him. A happy smile spread on his face, and he spoke to himself as was ever his wont:

"Why, I'll feel no sorrow to leave this earth when my proper times comes round—if Hannah comes wi' me. She kin sit next to me in the chariot and make my life as pleasant in Heaven as she has on earth!"

From that day on he never worried again and lived happily to the end of his life.

As for Hunn, who tried to make trouble for Josiah, this was writ on his tomb when he left this earth:

> "The flesh and bones of Samuel Hunn,
> Lie underneath this tomb.
> Oh let them rest in quietness
> Until the day of Doom."

The Giant Kingfisher
of Mount Riga

THEY tell a great story in the dark woods, the strange woods of Mount Riga, in Connecticut, where live the Raggies whose fathers were Nutmeg Yankees, blond Russians, and Swiss mountain men. Here is the story they tell.

When men came first from foreign countries to our rich New England, they worked together with the Yankees deep in the earth, digging iron, melting it in red-hot furnaces, and shipping the ore on wagons pulled by brown sleek oxen. Sundays they went to the big city to dance and play.

Came a time when the fires in the furnaces died, and there was no digging in the ground. People found more iron in other states in our land.

But the Yankees, the Russians, and the Swiss-Americans would not leave Connecticut. They couldn't. They had drunk the water of the magic well that stands in the middle of the town near the mountain of iron, and that kept them from going to any other place.

They became poorer and poorer—so poor, they were the poorest in the land.

One summer there was no rain at all, and the Raggies were even poorer than poor. Things just wouldn't grow, and animals fled to where there was rain and water.

Now amongst the Raggies was a sick man who had three sons. The oldest was ten, the second was nine, and the youngest, Frankie, was only eight.

One day there wasn't a crumb or a bone in that sick man's house, so he said to his sons:

"My sons, I know you're young and can't shoot no deer or bear, but maybe you can snare a small animal to still our hunger. Or maybe you can catch a sockeye salmon, that's the finest eatin' in all the world. Go, and may luck be wi' you."

So the three went, the oldest to the right, the middle one to the left, and the youngest straight ahead, straight into the shining sun.

At night they came back. The oldest brought a rabbit that was nothing but skin and bones, the middle one, a scrawny bird, and Frankie just brought some berries.

Asked the father, "How come, Frankie, you brought so little and your brothers so much?"

"Birds and beasts like to live, too, and I didn't have no heart to kill 'em."

The father didn't answer, but the brothers scowled

angrily and called him a hoot owl, a fool, and said he
was touched in the head.

When all the food was eaten the father called his sons
together and said:

"There's no bone or crumb in the house. Go out and
find food again, and luck'll be wi' you and you'll bring
somethin' to eat."

The three went off, and at night the oldest brought
a thin squirrel, the middle a scrawny bird, and Frankie
only some berries. The father, who loved the youngest
dearly, couldn't say a word, he was that sick.

When the food was eaten, and there was no bone or
feather left, the father told his sons again to go out and
find food. Said the eldest brother:

"Frankie, don't come back if you don't bring somethin' to eat, an' it's got to be better'n berries. We work,
an' you do nothin'."

The eldest brother went to the right, the younger to
the left, and Frankie, the youngest, went straight ahead,
straight into the shining sun.

He walked along the silent moss, he walked through
the dark woods, he walked long, until he came to Twin
Lakes. Dry berries were on bushes along the bank, and
a kingfisher sat on a limb of a willow right over the
water. Frankie looked at the funny bird with the big
head, the long bill, short tail, and chestnut feathers on
his sides, for a long time. Then he picked some berries,
ate them, and sat down under the willow where the bird
silently watched the water.

They sat there long, they sat there short, I cannot tell which, Frankie dreaming, the bird watching, when suddenly the bird splashed into the water and soon came up on the limb again . . . with nothing in its bill.

"Poor bird," cried Frankie aloud. "So you're hungry, too, and can't get nothing to eat."

The kingfisher opened her long bill, gave a loud and rattling cry, and said:

"My young are starving; there is only mud in the waters, no fish at all, not even frogs. My mate is flying over lakes and streams searching for food for our young ones to eat. If he doesn't bring anything they will starve. I haven't found a fish for them for days. No fish of any kind."

"There's no food in my home, either. My father sent me out to find some, and my brothers told me not to come back without it."

"I know your brothers. Day before yesterday one killed a kingfisher that lived not far from here and was too weak to fly. They are cruel."

"They were hungry. . . ."

No sooner were the words out of his mouth than there was a great rushing of wings in the air like a hurricane, and the sun was hidden from sight. In the sky was a giant kingfisher the like was never seen. His white-spotted wings near covered the top of the mountain, his long bill was the size of a ship's mast, and the white spots right before his eyes gleamed like two full silvery moons.

Behind him was the Raggie Country kingfisher who had gone off to find food for his young ones.

The giant bird landed near the willow, flattening hickories, yellow poplars, maple, and beech because the clearing wasn't large enough.

"I met the Great Kingfisher, the king of the king-fishers, flying north and told him we are starving. He's come to help us," cried the bird from Raggie land in a rattling voice.

"I've come to help you." Branches crackled and the brambles flew at the clattering voice of the giant bird.

"Our young haven't eaten for days, and if they have no food they'll surely die," said the mother bird.

"There's nothing to eat in our home, too," said Frankie. "My father's sick, and we three brothers are out to find food. My brothers said I mustn't come back if I don't bring a bird or beast."

The Great Kingfisher looked at Frankie and opened his long bill threateningly.

"He's a friend to bird and beast," said the mother bird quickly. "He could have killed me as did his brother one of us a few days ago, but he didn't."

"Everybody is hungry," said Frankie again, "birds and men."

Added the mother kingfisher, "We haven't been able to catch a fish for a long time . . . we need help quickly or it will be too late."

"I will bring you food," cried the giant bird loud enough to shake the trees. "I will give you food, too," he said looking at Frankie, "and your father will not starve; such food as you all like best. Soon you'll have the finest fish of all. Wait! Wait for me, I'll not be long."

He raised himself high on his giant wings, and once again the sun was hidden and the wood was dark. Then he winged his way far into the north.

It didn't take long, and it didn't take short, but the sun was low in the sky when the bird returned to where the boy and the two kingfishers were still waiting. He circled round and round, and each time he came over the water he opened his bill and dropped in the water the finest, fattest sockeye salmon ever seen. Fat, rich sockeye salmon found only far up north where the water is cold.

"You birds eat and feed your young, and you, boy, run home and tell your sick father and your brothers there'll be plenty to eat from now on. The lakes around Mount Riga, Bear Mountain way, Lime Rock, and Ore Hill will soon be full of the finest sockeye salmon that ever was." Then the mighty bird was off.

The kingfishers dived into the lake, came up, and flew home to feed the young, and Frankie raced home to tell the glad news.

When his brothers saw him empty handed they cried:

"It's you without anythin'. We told you . . ." but before they could finish the words, Frankie cried:

"I got no woodchuck, or deer, but I got good news. We'll all have enough to eat. The best kind of eating.

What father likes and what we like, too! Fine, fat sock-eye salmon, which is better 'n all the woodchuck an' deer."

"You're lyin'," cried the brothers.

"I'm not. Come, I'll show you where."

So the brothers took their rods and were off. And that night there was a feast in Frankie's home the like there wasn't for many moons.

While they were eating, the Great Kingfisher went back and forth bringing sockeye salmon in his great long beak and dropping them in every pond round Mount Riga, Bear Mountain, and Ore Hill.

The word spread quick how the Great Kingfisher had brought the Raggies good fish to eat. From that day on there was the finest sockeye-salmon fishing in lake and pond. No Raggie was ever hungry for fish, and no Raggie ever touched a kingfisher—the funny bird with the long bill, short tail, and the wobbly, weak-worn legs.

The Wise Men of Hebron

THE men of Hebron on the Hop River were as wise as the men of Gotham in England, for they, too, could do things the way they never were done before. The men of Gotham could gather sunshine in old rag-bags, and the men of Hebron could make a cannon . . . and thereby hangs a tale.

There was great rejoicing in Hebron town one day. The war against the French was over, the battles were won, and the Hebron heroes who had won the battles were on their way to home and land. So there was a long meeting in the town hall and great talk of how to celebrate the happy event.

Men and women spoke their minds. Some were for carpets strewn with roses, as in the fairy tales, but there were no carpets and few roses in Hebron on the Hop River. Some were for dancing maidens with timbrels and trumpets playing, as in the Bible. But there were not many dancing maidens in Hebron on the Hop River, nor timbrels, nay, not even a trumpet.

In the end one old sailor man, Seth Gordon, who had been to the wars at sea, spoke up and said:

"Every celebration in a war is celebrated with booming of shiny brass cannons. It's the proper way to welcome great soldiers coming home from the wars—I've heard many a shiny cannon booming for such occasion."

All agreed it was a fine thought and a proper one, and the only question now was to find a shiny brass cannon for the booming.

Now there had come to the town that day a young peddler loaded with tins and pans, oxhandles, hop poles, and notions to sell, who listened to the argument and thought he'd have a little game with the good people of the town.

Said he with a long face, though it was only in jest:

"Since you have no brass cannon, why not make one of wood? It'll roar as loud!"

"But what if the powder splits the wooden cannon into pieces?" asked one of the elders.

"Just tie it with iron hoops, the like you put round barrels. That'll surely hold the wood in place."

The words were said, and the deed was done.

The cooper of the town set to work that night, and every man from the highest to the lowest, even women and children, helped with a good will.

They felled a giant oak and chopped and chopped and chopped until it was hollowed out. Then they put stout iron hoops around the tree, and it truly looked like a cannon, if you had a mind to think it such.

They thanked the young fellow who sold the shiny pots and pans and gave them good ideas. He went on his way as happy as those he left behind. And to every town he came he told the tale of how the wise men of Hebron made a wooden cannon with which to shoot a welcome roar for the soldiers coming from the wars.

The cannon done, all the men, women, and children of Hebron and seven pair of Devon oxen dragged the wooden fieldpiece up the hill. On the summit they lashed it tightly to the trees and left a guard to watch so none would steal it.

Then they waited, but not too long. One day the warriors who'd fought against the French came home. The joy of all was as big as their giant cannon on the hill. The men were feasted with good food and gave in return a feast of adventure tales. Then all went happily to sleep until the next morning, when the real celebration would begin on the hill.

Few eyes closed that night for long, and early with the dawn young and old, rich and poor, dressed in their best, filled baskets with good food and fine drink and went up the hill where the cannon was.

From sunup to sunset they feasted on meats and pies and danced and sang songs of merry England, and when the stars appeared they were ready for the great event.

First the children's and women's ears were stuffed with wool lest the noise burst them open. Then the men, who had brought their powder horns full of powder, poured it in the cannon's wide mouth. After that the old sailor man who'd heard the booming of brass cannons on the sea fixed a long string of wool to set the wooden monster off.

The stars shone bright, and the pipers piped their song. Men ran way off, hiding behind trees and rocks, and women and children were ordered still farther away. Dogs were chased home lest they turn mad or die from fright. Then the old sailor man lit the string of lint with a flaring pine torch. It burned along the grass until it reached the cannon, and then—there was a crash! and flash! and flying of stone and wood, the like had not been seen since the day the tower of Babel fell. The giant wooden cannon with the iron hoops crashed apart, flying in all directions. It flung the good Hebron people into the meadows and fields. It lit up all the land as far as Florida and Canada.

The booming bang was heard clear across the ocean far as London, where the King of England sat eating pie, and some of the splinters from the oaken cannon flew right into his plate.

When the King learned that the noise and wooden splinters came from his Hebron subjects of Connecticut celebrating the English victory over France with a wooden cannon, he sent them one of shiny brass. But the cannon never reached the town. It was so heavy it sank in the deep wide ocean.

But the Hebron folks didn't mind it a bit, even as they didn't mind the bursting of their cannon. For the fame of their deed spread far and wide, in every place and every land, even as their cannon and its crash and noise had spread.

To this very day people still tell of the wooden cannon of Hebron town that made the biggest noise and the biggest crash ever made by any cannon in the world.

The Bee Man
and the Boundary Man

SOME hard hearts become kind and loving because they do a kind or a loving deed; some, because they **see** others do it. That's the way of the world.

In fair Connecticut, in the valley called Paradise, lived two men.

One was a stone-crusher. All day long he cracked and crushed hard rocks to make white dust which painters need for their paint. But in his heart there was kindness and love. When his work was done, he'd lie down in the grass where the red sun shone warm and where the perfume of the clover and flowers was sweet as Paradise.

The other was a boundary man.

Day in and day out he made boundaries for farmer men, sawmill men, and railroad men. He was a hard-hearted man, and at the end of the day he'd figure out how much strife and argument he raised between neighbors and friends about their boundary lines.

Now that boundary man didn't like the stone-crusher man one bit; no, not one bit.

One day the two met in the green fields. The boundary man scowled angrily, but the stone-crusher smiled kindly.

Said the boundary man:

"Heard ye give away the big clock ye bought from the peddler to Moses Dingle. Now he won't get up earlier than needs be in the mornin' to milk the cows."

"That I did," said the stone-crusher.

"And got no money for it!" said the boundary man.

"No, I didn't."

"Ye're a fool, and ye're poorer than a mouse in a white church. Ye'll always be poor. Look at me, I'm rich an' strong. When I'm through fixin' a boundary line people fight 'bout it all their lives."

"Yes, I've heard say ye're a cruel man an' yer heart is bound with three fences o' field stones. Some day kindness'll break them stone fences."

The boundary man jeered and jowled and said he'd fix him for his silly talk, and soon, to boot.

The day after, a big railroad man with a golden chain across his white vest came to the house of the boundary man. He wiped the sweat off his forehead and said:

"I need the land along the rocky hill."

"That land belongs to the biggest fool in all America," said the boundary man. He meant the stone-crusher man.

"It don't matter to whom it belongs," the railroad man replied. "I'll pay you a big price; you just fix the boundary right."

The boundary man prowled around the mossy wood and the flowery fields and little singing waters.

Then one day he and the railroad man came to the hut of the stone-crusher man.

"Yer boundaries an' fences are all wrong," said the boundary man. "Yer land belongs to the railroad man. Ye got to leave."

Said the stone-crusher man:

"Land can't be hid in a barn or locked in a chest. The land is mine an' yourn and every other man's as well. I'll go right now."

"Ye'll go without fighting yer claim in court?" cried the boundary man. "No one ever heard of such a thing. Ye must fight."

"I'll not fight; I'll go right now."

The railroad man was so surprised he went off in his train and wasn't seen in Paradise Valley for many, many years.

The boundary man too went off, telling all who would listen he'd found a fool who gave up land without going to court and judges.

"He must be a good man," cried many a one.

"Good or otherwise, he's a fool; good or otherwise,

he's a fool!" the boundary man muttered again and
again.

But everybody said the stone-crusher man was a man
with a peace-loving heart not to want fighting in court.

So many said it over and over again to the boundary
man that in the end he almost . . . almost . . . began
to believe it.

No sooner did he believe it, than he felt kind of lighter
inside, in his heart!

And why shouldn't he? Crk! One of the gray stone
fences around his heart had fallen away! But the other
two were still there.

All the valley was humming about the stone-crusher
man who had given up land without a fight. Even the
animals heard of it.

Said the Queen of the Bees of Paradise Valley:

"There's a man who works for love of work and
giving. Let him stop hammering the dusty rock and
come to live with us on fruit, and perfume, and honey."

The bees came in swarms to the stone-crusher man
and told him what the Queen had said.

So the stone-crusher man went up beyond Brown
Brook hilltop into the little valley filled with purple
clover, wild pink roses, honeysuckle, and millions of
other flowers. There he lived happily with the bees,
tending them and their hives, and people called him the
bee man instead of the stone-crusher man.

He gathered so much honey, anyone could come and

get it from him without pay. But the boys and girls who lived near by got most of it.

Now it so happened that one day the boundary man passed by while the bee man was giving away the honey to some children.

"So yer gettin' money from the children for the honey ye steal from the bees," cried the boundary man.

"I didn't steal no honey an' don't get money for it. Here, take some too—without money."

"I don't have to pay for it!" cried the boundary man.

"No, ye kin jest have it."

The boundary man took the pot of honey and ran off quickly. He was afraid the bee man would change his mind and ask for money. And, as he ran, the birds and the wind were singing over and over and over again:

> "The bee man gave you honey
> And never asked for money."

He heard the rhyme in his ears, then in his head, and then . . . in his heart, and suddenly he felt lighter!

And why shouldn't he? Crk! The second of the gray stone fences around his heart was broken!

From that day on, the boundary man often prowled around the valley where the bee man lived. He just couldn't tell why.

One day, when the sun shone brightly enough to set the world a-ringing, he met the bee man along the road. He was carrying an earthen pot of honey in one hand

and a bunch of daisies and black-eyed Susans in the other hand.

"Where ye goin'?" the boundary man growled.

"I'm goin' to give honey an' flowers to Steve's little daughter who can't walk a step."

"Always givin' things away—I suppose for nothin'," the boundary man growled again.

"Oh, no, not for nothin'. I'll get a glance from her happy eyes. I'll see her cheek glowin', an' I know she'll forget she can't walk in the meadow or run. . . . That's the brightest money in all the world."

The bee man went his way, humming a little song that sounded like the buzzing of the bees among the flowers, while the boundary man stood there looking after him.

He stood a long time just thinking of Steve's little daughter who couldn't walk a step and how the bee man was bringing her honey and flowers to make her happy.

A gray, bushy squirrel was running through the branches of an old maple tree.

"The squirrel kin run if it wants to, but Steve's little daughter must sit all the time. And the bee man brings her presents to make her happy."

He thought he heard someone say this. He kept on hearing it again and again. First in his ears, then in his head, and then . . . in his heart! Suddenly he felt very light! So light as he had never felt in all his life.

And why shouldn't he? Crk! The third gray stone fence around his heart was broken!

He ran to his house that stood near by where he had a garden full of tall, yellow and white dahlias and tore an armful off. Then he quickly raced after the bee man.

"Ho there, bee man!" he cried. "Ho there, wait for me!"

When the bee man saw the gleam in the eyes of the boundary man and the glow in his face, he knew at once what had happened.

"I want to go with you to Steve's little daughter an' bring her my dahlias," shouted the boundary man.

"I know you do," said the bee man.

So the two went together, talking and laughing. And when Steve's little daughter saw the two men coming to bring her gifts, she was twice as happy as she had been before.

From then on, the boundary man did not make false boundary lines that made people enemies, but he gave flowers not only to Steve's little daughter but to the passing railroad men or anyone who wanted them.

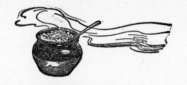

The Frogs of Windham Town

IN the olden days, in the gay days, the Wise Men of Windham were as famous as the Wise Men of Gotham for their love of fun and frolic and for their bantering and their jesting.

One hot afternoon they had a merry gathering on Windham Green playing games, eating and drinking, singing and dancing, instead of worrying about the French and Indian Wars people said were coming to our land.

When they tired of the games, they spoke of this and that, but mainly of the valleys on the Susquehanna River where life was even more pleasant than in Windham town.

Now amongst those present was old Jabez, from Boston Green, who frowned and fumed at the gay carryings-on.

He thought such merryment was a sin against the Lord and should never be. He argued with Colonels Dyer and Elderkin of Windham and told them they should be thinking of the coming war and the wrath of the Lord and praying day and night, instead of dallying and laughing.

"Dance a jig today, pay the Devil on the morrow," he warned them. But all arguments were of no avail, and the jollity of the Windham people kept on till late in the night. Then they went to sleep, happy and tired and with the peace of mind of angels.

They slept an hour or maybe three, when they were awakened by a most devilish noise, the like was never heard before. There were fiendish yells and screams'd make the blood turn white.

The good people of Windham leaped from under their covers and rushed out to see what the noise was about. They ran this way and that way and every way to learn the cause of the hubbub and commotion. But no one seemed to know the reason, save old Jabez. He stood right in the middle of the Green in a white night-shirt, his white hair flying in the wind, screaming and shouting loud enough to hear above the other noises:

"It's the wrath of the Lord crying against you! The Indians, nay, the Devil in person, has come to destroy all Windham like Sodom and Gomorrah in the Bible, for its merrymaking. Above all, they've singled out Colonel Dyer and Colonel Elderkin who are the leaders in the devilish gaieties. Listen close! listen well! and ye'll hear the fiendish cry, Dyer and Elderkin."

All listened and soon could truly hear a deep roaring and croaking, that sounded like "Dyer! Dyer! For

Dyer!" followed by a shrill piping and screaming: "Elderkin! Elderkin! For Elderkin!"

A great fear fell upon the people of Windham. They now believed old Jabez verily told the truth.

But valiant Colonel Dyer and Colonel Elderkin were not frightened by old Jabez' jabbering. They were not afraid of Indians or even of the Devil. They cried loud above the tumult:

"To your weapons! To arms!"

Every man, woman, and child ran into house and barn and returned with muskets and scythes, knives, and sticks, ready for battle with Indian or Devil.

Then the two brave colonels, leading all the town folk, marched around the Green many times while the screaming and the croaking never stopped. They marched and marched, but no enemy ever showed its face.

So they kept on marching till the rosy sun showed in the east and the noise and the fearful screeching grew less and less. The more light, the less noise and . . . less fear in the hearts of Windham folks.

Now they marched up the hill and down the valley until they reached the place from which the sounds were coming. It was at Swamp Brook, nearly dry from the lack of rain for many weeks. There they stopped, in great surprise. For they saw the cause of all the screaming and screeching, the cause of all their fears! And what do you think it was? FROGS! Nothing but frogs!

Around the pond were many bullfrogs croaking

weakly while many little frogs were scattered far and wide, silent and dead. The frogs had come to the pond and had battled for the water that was left. 'Twas their croaking noise that sounded so fearsome and frightening in the dark of the night.

The people of Windham stood and looked for a long, long time. Then Colonel Dyer said:

"Look ye, Master Jabez, these are the French and Indians and the Devil with which you frightened us."

"A pox on you, Master Jabez," added Colonel Elderkin. "We'll continue to be happy and merry, and don't you be telling us we'll be punished for it. The only thing that punishes us is fear. Go your way, Master Jabez, and leave us to our ways."

Master Jabez went his way angrily. But, ever since, people always tell the tale of the frogs that frightened Windham town one dark summer night.

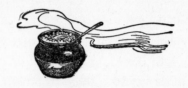

Haddam Witches

THE White-Magic Witches of East Haddam in Connecticut vexed the people there no end. They destroyed the finest cows and the best calves in a manner no one could explain, and that brought woe and sadness to every home in town, but most of all to Daniel Smith and his family.

They were kind but poor people and had lost a fine calf from the strange sickness. Now their only cow was ailing, and, if she too would die, they'd be poorer than the poorest.

One day they were sitting sad and silent when there came a knock at the door and in came Timothy from near-by Haddam. He was loaded with tins and pans to sell, but he did not come to sell them any wares. He only came to see young Rachel, Daniel's brown-eyed daughter.

Timothy heard the tale of woe and said:

" 'Tis done by witches. Everyone says so, and I say so, too. Something must be done to stop 'em."

"But who'll do the doing?" asked pretty Rachel. "Everyone is scared o' witches."

"I'll do it," said Timothy fearlessly. "I was born in Ireland with a caul on me head that means luck. I travel through woods and valleys selling me wares, and I'm not afraid of anythin' flyin' in the air or crawlin' on the earth."

"I know you're not," said Rachel, and her eyes shone brightly. "But you must take care so no harm comes to you." Then she bade him good-by and Godspeed.

"Ye'll soon hear from me. God bless ye!" said Timothy.

He went over rough roads and over stony roads toward the Devil's Hop Yard, which was not far from the town, where people said witches often came.

The sky grew dark, the wind blew hard, and the trees bent low, but that did not frighten Timothy at all. It was just the right kind of weather for witches.

The sky grew darker, the wind blew harder, and the trees bent lower when he came to the great big oak right near the Devil's Hop Yard. It stood still, naked, and leafless since the day a crow sat on its branches bowing east, north, south, and west, and crowing hoarsely seven times. Then he came to the Devil's Hop Yard. It was a great stony field strewn with gray-black rocks in which the fierce rains and wild storms had made deep holes just like smooth pots. In them the witches brewed strong-smelling hops and sometimes cooked ripe brown beans with salty pork, which all the people of New England, and witches, too, love dearly.

Around the stone potholes danced the seven witches of East Haddam, screaming and screeching worse than a gale tearing through the trees. Their red hoods and black shawls flew around like torn sails on a black sea, and they howled a wild gibberish song. Around them sat their black cats with glowing eyes.

Do you think that frightened Timothy even a little mite? Not at all. He went right in their midst and screamed louder than all of them.

"Ye're all happy; I want to be happy, too," and he began beating the shiny pots and pans he had for sale. He did not think it was wise to tell right then what he came for.

The East Haddam witches saw him dance and thought he was their own kind, so the head witch screamed:

"Come with us to the cave in Mount Tom where our Master sits and help us battle the Haddam witches."

"Battle the Haddam witches? And, pray, why?"

The witches shouted and screamed with laughter.

"Don't ye know? Haven't ye heard of the dying calves in East Haddam? That's our doing. Now the Haddam witches want to do it. So our Master lets us battle for this favor on the witches' Sabbath night, and those who win have the right to do mischief. Come and help us in the fight. Show us what ye kin do."

"Oh, so that's the grand game. I'll come gladly and see what I kin do."

And he meant the very words. Now he knew who made the mischief, and he would see what he could do to stop it. He didn't know just how he'd do it. But he put faith in the Lord to help him, and in his Irish luck.

The East Haddam witches mounted their black cats and broomsticks, took Timothy with all his pots and pans, and flew straight to Mount Tom, straight to the big cave.

There was a sight to see!

The great cave was lit by a giant gleaming carbuncle set in the top, and under it, on a seat of shimmering sapphire, was the wild Indian Devil Chief, a wand of carved wood in his hand.

In front of him sat the Black-Magic Witches of Haddam, covered with red hoods and black shawls, waiting grimly for the fray. No sooner did they see their rivals from East Haddam than up they leaped, and the battle was on, with screeching, screaming, tearing, and ripping.

But as for Timothy, he crept behind the throne quickly to be out of the way of sticks and rocks and claws and stones.

"Battle! Battle!" cried the Indian. "Fight for the power to kill the cattle the white men need; then they'll leave the land."

When Timothy heard this he knew just what to do.

He came right before the Indian Chief and said:

"Ye'll never drive the white men from the land by

killing their cattle. They'll bring other cattle from across the sea. There's no end to cattle over there. Stop the killin' and find another way. I'm yer friend, the witches brought me here."

The witches screamed and screeched, and sticks and stones and clothes and bones flew all around. Said the Devil Chief:

"How can I drive them from the land? Tell me another way, and I'll stop the witches from killing."

"Ye must do somethin' bigger."

"I can make big noises," said the Indian.

"That's fine," cried Timothy. "That's just the proper thing. Make big noises, and the white men'll be frightened and leave the land."

The witches screamed and screeched, and sticks and stones and clothes and bones flew all around.

"Stop the battling," cried the Indian. "You'll kill no more cattle. Stop your noises. I'll make better noises."

That made both the Black-Magic Witches of Haddam and the White-Magic Witches of East Haddam madder than hornets on the warpath, and they began battling worse than before. They screamed and screeched, they yelled and yelped, and sticks and stones and clothes and bones flew all around worse than ever.

The Indian Devil grew angry to see his order disobeyed.

He raised his wooden wand on high, and the light of the great carbuncle went out. There came a thundering noise that shook the earth and rocked the mountain and swayed the trees and shook the houses.

The witches were frightened and flew away never to return, and the people of Haddam and East Haddam were frightened, too, but they didn't run away, as Timothy knew they wouldn't. They were just frightened for a little time and then were not frightened at all.

The dying of the cattle stopped, and the people were happy as they hadn't been for a long time.

Then Timothy and Rachel were married and lived happily ever after.

But the noises in Mount Tom came back again and again. For the Indian Devil tries again and again to frighten the white men from the land. But you know he can't.

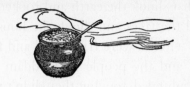

Diamond Jim and Big Bill

UP in Paradise, in Connecticut, the Nutmeg State, Big Bill was the best fisherman that ever was, and from morning to night he caught every kind of fish that swam in ponds or leaped in streams. But his greatest joy was to catch gleaming spreckled trout that played in the shadowy pools of dark waters.

One day he caught the biggest, fattest trout in the land. And this is how it happened.

There lived, at that time, a very rich man in a great city who always wanted bigger, more, and better things than anyone else had. He wore not just one diamond, but he had them stuck on his shirt and cuffs, and so people called him Diamond Jim.

One evening Diamond Jim and many of his gent and lady friends were sitting in a great dining room lit by a thousand lights. Gypsies played sweet music, and many people were eating and dancing. Next to Diamond Jim's table sat four men from Canada and Maine, who were boasting great boasts about the big salmon and trout they had eaten in the Canadian inns.

Diamond Jim heard this, looked on his plate where lay a little trout, and saw that truly it was a little, little fish. So he roared out loud as a cannon for Oscar, the big boss in that dining room, to come to his table, quick.

Oscar came with a smiling face and a long black frock coat and snow-white shirt.

"What is your pleasure, Mister Diamond Jim?" he asked.

"My pleasure," shouted Jim for all to hear in the great room, but mainly for the men next to his table, "my pleasure is to have in three days the biggest, fattest trout that was ever caught in our great country. Bigger than anything that was ever caught in Canada or any other place. I want it right here for the party I'm going to have. I want all the Canucks from Canada and all the loggers from Maine to see the kind of trout you can serve in your great dining room, Oscar."

Oscar in his black frock coat and snow-white shirt bowed low and said:

"Mister Diamond Jim, you'll have in our elegant dining room, three days from now, the biggest, fattest trout that was ever served in any dining room in the whole wide world. I'll send a telegram to Big Bill up in Connecticut, who is the finest trout catcher from the Atlantic to the Pacific. I know he'll catch for you exactly the kind of trout you want. All you need do is just bring your lady and gentlemen friends here three days from now."

That night the telegraph wires to Connecticut

zoomed and whistled back and forth, and telegraph poles
bent sideways and frontways like twigs in the wind,
with the messages between Oscar and Big Bill about the
trout.

The next day Bill hitched his fine brown mare to a
long pole wagon. On the seat next to him was a tin box
filled with ten dozen young field mice, and the strongest
fishing rod ever seen. He was on his way to the Shepaug
River to catch the finest trout in all the land for Diamond Jim to eat.

At the river he let his horse feed along the bank while
he walked up and down, up and down, rod in hand, to
find the right kind of trout. It took maybe an hour,
maybe five, when suddenly he knew he had just what
he wanted. His line pulled as if a young whale had
caught. In all his fishing days he never felt such heavy,
fierce pulling.

For hours and hours the battle between Big Bill and
the giant bull trout went on. The red sun sank lower
and lower, and still the fight went on and on, only
slower and slower. Then it ended altogether. But when
Bill tried to pull the fish out of the water he was so tired
from the pulling that he just couldn't. Quickly he made
a rolling boat of logs, tied his log chain to it, and had his
strong horse pull the fish out of the water and into the
wagon.

He raced to the railroad station, packed the giant fish
in a box full of ice, and put it on the fastest train on the
line. The train raced so fast the iron rails became red

hot and had to wriggle to the river to cool off. Meanwhile Big Bill told Oscar, over the zooming telegraph wires, to get ready to cook the biggest, fattest bull trout in all the United States.

That night, which was the third night, Diamond Jim came with a great company of elegant ladies and high-hatted gents to the big dining room full of glistening lights and dancing people. The Canucks from Canada were there, too, and the loggers from Maine, for Diamond Jim had bet them they'd see the biggest trout fish they'd ever seen.

All of a sudden the gypsy band played wild music and the people got up from their chairs, for in came Oscar followed by eight men carrying a giant fish on a giant silver platter. The giant fish was far too big for the table, so Oscar cut it in great fat slices. Everyone got a thick chunk even though there were seventy-three tables with six people sitting around each table.

The Canucks from Canada and the loggers from Maine said they truly had never seen a trout that size anywhere and never tasted one so good. They were mighty glad to lose their bet for the pleasure they had.

But Diamond Jim was the happiest man of all. He always wanted the biggest and the best, and he got it this time.

So he gave the biggest presents of gold to Oscar, who knew how to please him, to the cook, who knew how to cook for him, and to Big Bill, who knew what kind of fish to catch for him.

The
State of
RHODE
ISLAND
"Little Rhody"

Providence

Chipuxee

Newport

Donald McKay

Puffing Potter's Powerful Puff

IN the days of brave men and brave deeds in Rhode Island, a man lived there proud as a Narragansett pacer, who could puff and blow harder than any man could puff or blow in all the land. He was over six feet tall and weighed near three hundred pounds, and his name was Elisha Potter. Puffing Potter would have been a better name. His blowing could set a ship sailing to the moon and start Rocky Mountain rocks dancing "Buffalo Girls Will You Come Home Tonight." His puffing'd bend old trees like young saplings and swing houses through the air the same as young tornadoes from Arizona.

And, since like seeks like, you'd be sure to find Puffing Potter wherever Governor Fenner of Rhode Island was. For the brave Governor was almost as big as Potter and twice as round, and could roar decisions in a voice that could be heard as far as Boston. When he delivered a speech it sounded like an earthquake just born, and when he raised his voice in anger you'd think eleven bulls were fighting in a red flannel circus.

They were always together, these two, each trying to outdo the other in puffing and shouting.

One fine summer's day in July, the General Assembly met in Little Rest to discuss the great affairs of state. That town got its name for a sad reason. There were so many lawyers there, who were forever arguing so much about useless laws, that the townspeople had very little rest day or night.

At the opening of the meeting, Governor Fenner was making a grandiloquent speech about the wonders of Narragansett County in a voice that could be heard in Boston Bay. When he came to a most clever remark, a poor little snipper-snapper Providence County lawyer who got into the Assembly, the Lord only knows how, made a slurring remark about Narragansett and its wonders. Governor Fenner looked at him haughtily, and Puffing Potter looked at him in surprise. Then the Governor went on with his fine speech.

After a time, he spun a pun finer than China silk about the people of Narragansett County. For the second time, the little snipper-snapper lawyer made a low-down remark fit for a tavern and not a Rhode Island Assembly. The Governor, a gentleman to the last echo of his voice, who wouldn't deny freedom of speech even to a mole in the earth, just glared at the silly toad-hopping law-monger and continued his golden words. But his friend, Puffing Potter, got kind of mad at the audacity of the individual. His chest began to heave like the bellows of a forge, and his body bent forward slightly in the direction where the fellow was sitting.

When the Governor came to the most flowery part of his oratory, telling one and all that Narragansett was as fine as the Garden of Eden if not finer, the little windbag lawyer cackled out a sickly, creaky laugh.

That was just one too many for Potter. His chest began going like a Santa Fe engine in a race. His head bent in the direction of that little two-legged shrimp of a lawyer, and, before the Governor even had a chance to get angry, Potter let loose the angriest, fiercest, snorting puff of his life. It was a full-blooded, genuine, chest-tornado heave.

The walls shook, men quaked, the building rocked, and the little lawyer who stood in the way of the puff flew straight and swift through the open window. Outside he kept going. Only by the providence of the good Lord who watches over all, the good as well as the foolish, he landed straight on old Robinson's gingerbread-and-apple cart that stood under a buttonwood tree about a half a mile from the Assembly house.

There he lay, still as a mouse, all doubled up. Old Robinson thought it was one of the flying African monkeys that had come that morning with the circus and had escaped from its cage. But on looking more carefully at the head he calculated, with Rhode Island smartness, there couldn't be enough brains in that head lying there for a monkey, but just enough for a lawyer.

From that day on, Providence County chose men for the Assembly of the right size and fitting profession, who could stand up properly when Puffing Potter puffed any of his powerful puffs.

The Rich Lady
and the Ring in the Sea

IN a grand wide mansion on Moonstone Beach, right by the ocean wide, lived a rich, proud lady. She had a fine husband, that lady had, she had lands and jewels, and she had slaves and ships. But one thing she did not have, and that was sweet kindness in her heart.

One day rich Mistress Perry, that was her name, was walking along the yellow sands of the shore while the sun shone brightly on the blue water. She was dressed in silks and satins, by her side ran her little dog, and she carried a silken parasol over her head. Came by an old woman dressed in rags and tatters and a plaid, torn shepherd shawl over her gray hair.

"Please, rich lady," the old woman begged, "give me some food. Give me some shelter. I am so tired and hungry."

"Keep away from me," Mistress Perry cried. "Keep away from me. I can't be bothered with your kind." And she began walking away quickly.

"Some day you may be poor," cried the old woman,

"and I hope a lady will treat you with greater kindness than you treat me."

"Poor I'll never be, old woman," Mistress Perry replied haughtily. "Poor I'll never be, for I have all the riches a woman can possess."

"Some day you may be poor," the old woman said again. "Poor as I am, and I hope people will be kinder to you than you are to me."

Mistress Perry looked angrily at the old woman, took the golden wedding ring from her finger, and flung it far out into the rolling sea.

"Even as this ring can never return from the sea, so can I never be poor," she said.

Then she ran home and told the tale to all. But the old woman muttered sad words and went along the hot burning sand.

Soon after, there was a great feast in Mistress Perry's home, with silver spoons and china plates. Rich and famous guests from far and from near were there talking of this and that. There was every kind of meat and every kind of fish brought to the table, and amongst them a giant brown-broiled striped sea bass. Squire Perry cut that fish open, and there, in it, was Mistress Perry's wedding ring. The guests were silent, and the lady of the house turned pale as a blossom, but she did not say a word.

The summers and the falls, the winters and the springs came, and years and years rolled by. Squire Perry lost venture after venture, and his harvests failed. His cattle sickened, his ships were lost, the barns burned down, and Master and Mistress Perry became poorer and poorer.

In the end Squire Perry died, and Mistress Perry was as poor as was the old woman she had met on Moonstone Beach years and years ago, who had told her she, too, might beg for charity.

For charity Mistress Perry begged, and people were kinder to her than she had been to the old women. Instead of driving her away, they helped her. Instead of harsh, unkind words, they spoke gently and lovingly.

Mistress Perry never forgot this. In her prayers she thanked the Lord for it and thought humbly and contritely of the old woman.

The Cat Inspector

THEY talk and they tell about a man in Little Rest town who wasn't liked by any boy or girl, woman or man, in all of Rhode Island because he was a Cat Inspector. His name was Lisha, and he was the only Cat Inspector in Rhode Island, in all America, and maybe in all the world. For who ever heard of a Cat Inspector except in Rhode Island?

For clothes he wore a dark blue coat covered with gilded cord, on his head he had a bright blue cockaded hat, and in his hand he carried a silver marker. With this he marked every cat he could catch so that all the world knew it was a Rhode Island cat.

From morning to night he ran after cats in the street and cats in the alleys. He even ran after pet cats right into the homes of people so he could mark them properly as true Rhode Island cats. That is why nobody liked Lisha, the Cat Inspector.

Even little Quaker boys and girls, who were taught morning, noon, and night to love everything and everyone with brotherly love, didn't love that Cat Inspector. Least of all Tommy, who lived down in Narragansett.

Tommy's long white wooden house stood not far from the sea, and in it were fifteen cats of every size and shade. This, not counting four or five litters of kittens tumbling and playing with strings of wool and bits of calico. Tommy loved every one of those cats, the big ones and the little ones. He never had any use for Lisha the Cat Inspector, you can be sure of that.

One Sunday morning, Tommy tore his trousers. He said it was the fault of the nail in the cow barn, and so he couldn't go to the "Meeting House," as the church was called by the Quakers. Everybody went to "Meeting," but Tommy stayed home.

He had no sandalwood boxes, monkeys, or parrots to play with, as children of Rhode Island seamen had. So he decided to play with his fifteen cats, and maybe a few of the kittens, too.

He called Abe, the colored man, who was his friend, and the two began catching the cats and putting them in an upper chamber that was empty.

It wasn't an easy task, you can be sure. The cats didn't want to be caught and put in a dark room when the sun was shining brightly in garden and field.

In the end they got fourteen of them, all the black ones, the white ones, the yellow ones and striped ones, and those that had many colors. The fifteenth cat, a yellow one with tiger stripes, a big square head, and green eyes, just wouldn't get caught.

"Them's 'nuf cats foh playin' on a mohnin'," said Abe.

"Maybe thee is right," said little Tommy.

Then Tommy and Abe began playing with the cats round and round the empty room.

The floor creaked, the cats squealed, Tommy screamed, and Abe reeled. It was great fun, the kind any boy would love. Tommy and Abe had a grand old time.

At first the cats didn't seem to mind it, but soon they did and wanted to get out of the room. They thought it was time to stop; but Tommy didn't.

Now, in that large empty room there was a wide stone fireplace. The biggest of the cats found it first and, looking up the chimney, saw the clear blue sky. Up she climbed along the sooty walls.

All the other cats, seeing this, followed quickly, clawing and climbing through the soot.

It just so happened that Lisha, the Cat Inspector of Rhode Island, in his gold-braided coat and cockade hat, and Kit Potter, the Tower Hill coopersmith, were walking along toward Tommy's house at that very hour.

They were talking about this and that.

Said Kit to Lisha:

"Why don't you stop being a Cat Inspector and turn to an honest trade?"

Said Lisha to Kit:

"Because cat inspecting is as fine a trade as any. Just look at my golden coat and my silver rod. And all I have to do is to catch Rhode Island cats and inspect them."

Said Kit to Lisha:

"I wouldn't want to inspect cats at all, I'd be afraid. Don't you know that witches often turn to cats?"

They had then come right before Tommy's house.

"Meow! Meow!" screamed a cat as big as a catamount with fiery eyes, leaping from the chimney on top of Tommy's house. She looked like a witch, all covered with black soot.

"Meow! Meow! Meow! Meow! Meow! Meow!" and black soot-covered cat after black soot-covered cat leaped out of the chimney into the morning sunshine. They truly looked like wild witches on a Sabbath dance.

Lisha and Kit stopped as though they were turned to stone with fright.

"It's witches!" screamed Kit. "They're after you, Lisha, for chasing the cats of Rhode Island!" And he began running with all his legs.

"It's sure black witches," screamed Lisha, frightened to death and running after Kit.

They ran and they ran, they ran and they ran, until they reached Kit Potter's house by the brook. There they fell down unable to say a word for a long time.

When they could speak they told each and everyone that five hundred black witches or maybe more in the form of black cats were leaping out of Tommy's house after Lisha, to punish him for chasing the cats of Rhode Island.

From that day on Lisha would not be Cat Inspector anymore. And since Rhode Islanders, as well as all other New Englanders, were scared of witches in those days, there has never been another Cat Inspector anywhere in New England.

Haley, maley, tippety fig.
Tiny, tony, tombo, nig.
Goat, throat, country vote,
Tiny, tony, tig.

The tale is done,
'Twas lots of fun.

The Devil in Red Flannel

THERE once lived a farmer, Benny, and his wife, Debby, who tended to their work from morning to night, minded their own place, and followed the ways of the Lord. For that, they thrived and grew richer all the time. They grew so rich that the townspeople, who were lazy and spent their time gossiping, said the Evil One was helping them to greener crops and fatter sheep.

Now there was one little sheep that Debby loved more than all the others. A white, woolly creeper sheep it was, with short legs and long snowy wool.

My, how she loved that sheep! In the morning, she combed it, at noon she fed it, and at night she tucked it away to sleep. She even put pretty ribbons around it on Sundays and played with it. When people saw this, they were sure that Debby was a witch.

"Some witches love cats," they said, "and some love creeper sheep."

One day, early in March, the sun was shining bright and the sheep went to graze in the meadow, nozzling

231

for young grass. But soon a great, wild snow storm arose. It snowed so thick and blew so hard that you couldn't see in front of your eyes. Benny the farmer rushed out, gathered the sheep, and drove them into the shelter.

Alas and alack! The next morning, when Debby went to look for her favorite sheep, it was nowhere in the flock. She ran out into the fields, into the meadows, but she saw only snow and ice. She cried and she wept and she wept and she cried, but all her crying and weeping did not bring the sheep back.

Benny, her husband, promised her three nice new baby creeper sheep, but she only wanted her own sheep back again.

So the days passed, while the wind blew cold, and the earth was covered with snow.

One day, like every day and for the thousandth time, Debby and Benny went out looking for the sheep.

They looked and they looked, but there was no sheep in that white world of snow and ice. They were on their way home, walking across a meadow, when they saw a tiny breathing hole, the kind of hole often made by an animal's warm breath when it is buried under snow and ice.

"Maybe it's my darling sheep," cried Debby.

They chopped the snow and ice with might and main, and there *was* Debby's little creeper sheep, shivering, quaking, bleating, and blowing sadly, and . . . its long white wool completely gone. The poor sheep had been under the snow and ice six long days and, having no other food, had eaten its own white wool.

Debby carried the beastie home in her arms, fed it warm milk and bread, and covered it with a warm blanket.

Every day the little sheep grew stronger.

The sun shone warmer, ice and snow melted away, and all the sheep played in God's sunshine looking for young grass. But the little creeper sheep did not go out. It was too cold without its woolly coat. It bleated and cried all the time. Debby thought and thought about it until she had a good thought.

"I'll make a jacket for you so you can go out with the rest of the sheep," she cried.

Quickly she took an old red flannel petticoat and cut and sewed. Soon she had a nice little jacket fitting the creeper sheep, covering it all over except for its four legs and black little snout.

"It'll look funny on you, my darling little sheep," she said, "but it'll be nice and warm, and you can be in God's sunshine and play with the other sheep."

Well, the sheep was a sight! If you had traveled up and down the length of America and maybe Europe you couldn't have seen a funnier sight.

But the little animal didn't mind it a bit. It gamboled in the sun, nozzled the ground, and was warm as a feather bed in its red flannel jacket.

One day Hester, the town's worst gossip, passed by Debby's house. No sooner did she see the strange creature, four hairy legs and a black hairy snout sticking out of the red flannel jacket, than she ran quaking and screaming:

"The Devil dressed in red flannel is in Debby's field."

When she came to the village all tuckered out from the running she was telling one and all that the Devil dressed in red flannel was dancing with Debby in the meadow.

The people took sticks and stones, scythes and brooms, and even old flintlock guns, and ran to burn the witch and the Devil in red flannel at one and the same time. They weren't going to have any witches in their town. Not they!

So they ran through the woods and fields, the Mayor in front, a big hammer in his hands.

They came to Debby's home. It was noon by then, and she and her husband were eating bean soup and bread. The sheep was in the kitchen, too, munching on a crust of old bread.

"Come out, you witch, and bring the Devil in red flannel, too!" a hundred voices screamed.

Debby and Benny came to the door to see what was wrong. They saw the crowd, fury in their eyes and clubs in their hands.

"What's eating you now?" Debby asked, for, having done no wrong, she wasn't afraid of anyone.

"You're a witch," they screamed at her. "The Devil in red flannel is with you, but we'll put an end to both of you. Hester saw both of you."

"Oh, so that's it," snapped good Debby at them. "She saw me, did she! Evil does as evil thinks. You're a pack of silly fools. I'll show you the Devil in red flannel!"

She pulled out the sheep, that stood behind her, by the ear.

"Here is the Devil of whom you are frightened, you blind fools!" she cried. "It's my poor sheep that lost its wool. I made a jacket for it from an old red flannel petticoat so it wouldn't freeze." And she and her husband laughed loudly.

Well, the people of the town surely felt silly. They went home, and no one said a word, they were that ashamed.

From then on they never called old Debby or any women a witch, for they always remembered the sheep in red flannel they thought was a Devil.

Mysteries of the Sea

THE fine ship "Seabird" was sailing the deep blue sea, but things on board were not what they should be. The ship was beautiful with its grand white sails and rich full cargo, but the captain and the crew had gained the cargo dishonestly from the Indians and Spaniards of Honduras, in South America. And evil follows evil deed.

At first the voyage was prosperous. The winds blew strong, and the sun shone clear, but the captain and the crew were forever quarreling. The more they quarreled, the less favorable the winds blew. And, when there was almost open mutiny, the sky was black and cold, and the winds howled angrily.

One dark night, when the "Seabird" tossed about on the billowing waves like a broken reed, the sailor high in the lookout saw a strange light in the distance. He looked hard, and every minute the light grew larger and larger until he saw it was a burning ship. A great ship all in a blazing fire: sails, tackle, masts, rigging, jibs, and hull, all were in fierce leaping flames—fierce flames, yet not fierce enough to burn the wooden ship to cinders. The crew and captain had come up, and they all stood silent and dumb with fright. Suddenly the skipper cried:

"The 'Palatine' ship!"

There were cries from the others.

"The crew starved the passengers to death.—The captain was murdered.—The crew deserted the ship.—The ship struck a reef.—They couldn't tow her in.—Fire was set to the ship.—The burning ship drifted out to the sea.—A mad woman was forgotten.—She shrieked while the ship was burning.—Listen! You can hear the mad woman screeching.—It means disaster.—It means bad luck.—It always means bad luck!—Death and ill luck follow the ship that sights the burning 'Palatine'!"

The blazing ship sailed by them, and it was hard to tell which was louder, the screeching of the mad woman or the screeching of the winds.

All night long and all the next day, the winds howled as if in angry pain. The rain came through the air, whipping the whirling vessel and the frightened crew.

Next midnight, the burning ship came again out of the stormy dark and passed them by. Icy fear crept into the hearts of captain and crew; a thick shadow fell over them. Few spoke, and their steps were heavy. The ship tossed and lurched about on the waters like a rotten, old cork.

With black dread, captain and crew waited for the third night. Again the burning ship raced by them. The mad woman still shrieked. They could see her running about with streaming hair on that burning ship that never burned down. Captain and crew looked on with wild eyes, but their hands were limp while the storm raged like a tornado. No one could control the wheel. Afar, dark threatening rocks suddenly loomed out of the waves.

"Man the boats! She'll hit the reefs!" the captain cried. The boats were lowered, and soon every man was gone. But they forgot a red tomcat the crew had picked up in Honduras and a small black spaniel which had come all the way from Rhode Island.

The boats disappeared in the dark night and were never, never seen again.

The next morning the sea was calm and the sun shone clear and warm while the red tomcat and the little black spaniel played happily on the empty boat. The red tomcat and the little black spaniel began talking to each other in their own language.

Said the cat: "Why did they all leave?"

Said the dog: "I am very unhappy about it."

Said the cat: "They shouldn't have deserted the ship."

Said the dog: "Something frightened them."

Said the cat: "Well, we have enough to eat and drink."

Said the dog: "We must bring the ship right back home. Right back into Easton Beach in Rhode Island."

Said the cat: "That was the crew's job. They ran away. We have enough to eat. Why worry about the ship?"

Said the dog: "It's our duty. The food won't last forever."

Said the cat: "Let us wait till the food is finished."

Said the dog: "No! We must start for home at once."

Said the cat: "I say no!"

Said the dog: "Now, if we start quarreling, we'll do the same as our masters and get into the same kind of trouble."

The red tomcat couldn't argue that, so he gave in. The dog guided the ship with his paws and snout, and the Lord who watches over those who love peace guided the animals and guarded the ship. They sailed on in the shining sun while sea gulls skimmed and danced on the green-blue sea.

One fine day, the people on the shore of Easton in Rhode Island saw a big ship coming full sail into port. Yet there was no sign of human life to be seen anywhere on the deck. The ship went easily through the breakers as if guided by invisible hands, and the keel came gently onto the sand.

Men, women, and children ran onto the ship and found only a dog sitting near the steering wheel while a red tomcat sat in the cabin near the galley stove on which a coffee pot was boiling gently.

They looked high and they looked low, but nowhere was there a sign of crew or captain, nor was ever a sign of them found. And so the burning "Palatine" and the crewless "Seabird" have remained mysteries of the sea ever since.

Old Man Elias
and the Dancing Sheriff

THE sheriffs are as hard as wood;
In chunks I'd chop them if I could.
So say the farmers of New England.

Truly, they are hard men without pity for man or beast. But one time a farmer, Old Man Elias, got the best of a sheriff and made him dance, to boot.

Old Man Elias, with his long white beard and horny hands, worked hard in the fields and woods to keep home and hearth together. But for all that he had little to show, he was ever so poor.

One day, while he was cutting hay in the meadow and the sweat was falling in drops from his brow, there came along the sheriff.

"Old Man 'Lias," said the sheriff, "ye owe three dollars fer Old Tom's pig, an' if ye don't pay I'll take ye straight t' jail."

"Don't owe three dollars t' no one; the pig wasn't

any good," said Old Man Elias. "An' any man who says so, don't tell the truth. Ain't got three dollars anyway, so I couldn't pay it if I had a mind t'."

"Then t' jail ye go," the hard-hearted sheriff said.

"T' jail I'll go, though I ain't pleasurin' the thought," said Old Man Elias, "but first I'd like t' go t' the Squire an' get the money he owes me for cuttin' the hay in the meadow."

To the Squire they went, and he gave Old Man Elias five brand new silver dollars.

"Now ye've enough money t' pay the three dollars," the sheriff said. "An' ye kin stay out o' jail."

"T' jail I go," Elias said. "I don't owe no three dollars, and I couldn't pay it if I had a mind t', for I need the five silver dollars t' eat in jail."

He began trudging along the road while the sun shone hot and burning.

"Gosh 'n' fishhooks! ye don't have t' eat in jail if ye ain't in it. An' in jail ye don't have t' be if ye pay me three silver dollars now," said the sheriff.

"T' jail ye said I must go, an' t' jail I'll go. I'll need five silver dollars for my food," said Old Man Elias slowly.

The day was getting hotter and hotter, and the road was long. The sheriff was tired and hungry, and Elias walked so slowly they wouldn't reach jail for at least another day.

"Old man 'Lias," the sheriff snorted, "I never meant t' take ye t' jail. I only said so t' get the three dollars.

Ye don't have t' go t' jail. Besides, I've an errand t' do on the opposite road."

"Ye arrested me, Sheriff, an' t' jail I go."

"Please go home, 'Lias," begged the sheriff. "I told ye I've business further down which'll be t' my gain. There's no gain in ye, only sweat."

"Sheriff, I'll not be bribed," cried honest Old Elias. "I'm a straight man, an' t' jail I go."

They trudged along slowly, very, very slowly. Old Man Elias whistled a tune, but not the sheriff. He was a stout man and sweated like a full kettle on a cold day, while the flies stung him, the hornets plagued him, and the sun roasted him.

So they came to a bridge which ran over a deep river. On the other side of the bridge was a fork in the road, one going to the right and one going to the left. The left led to the jail, the right to where the sheriff wanted to go.

The sheriff stopped.

" 'Lias," the sheriff cried, "here's the road ye must take. Go back t' home. Ye don't have t' go t' jail."

"T' jail ye came t' take me, an' t' jail I'm a-goin'," Old Man Elias said.

"I beg ye, 'Lias, don't go t' jail," the sheriff pleaded.

"Well, seein' it's ye beggin'," said Old Man Elias with a twinkle in his eyes, "I'll do it—but first ye got ter do sumpin fer me. We old 'uns think seein' a sheriff dancin' on a bridge with water runnin' under 't 'll bring good luck fer a year and a day. I need good luck, fer I'm an old man workin' the day long. So if ye dance on the bridge, while I sing 'Ol' Cha'm'ny Fair,' I'll go home with a year o' luck an' not t' jail, an' ye kin go your way."

The sheriff didn't like this in the least.

"Good airth 'n' sea! yer head's full o' bees," he shouted.

"Ef ye grudge an old man a little luck," said Old Man Elias, "I'll go straight t' jail."

The sheriff saw no way out, so he looked about to make sure none saw him, and walked onto the bridge.

Old Man Elias began singing "Old Chalmouny Fair" in a high cracked voice, and the sheriff started dancing. The sun shone hot, the flies buzzed fierce, and the sheriff hopped up and down in his heavy boots while Old Man Elias kept on singing his song.

It was a sight for sore eyes. The birds and the beasts, the flies and the bees, and one or three farmers passing on the road had a grand old time seeing the funny sight.

When Old Man Elias got tired of singing he stopped.

"I'm a-goin' t' home, Sheriff, and thanks fer bringin' me luck fer a year an' a day. As fer ye, I hope ye have the same kind o' luck fer a year an' a day, and every year after, without takin' an honest man t' jail."

A New Way to Cure
Old Witch-hunting

ONCE there was an old man by the name of Murphy who had come from Massachusetts to live in Rhode Island. Since he came from a state where people were in the habit of hunting witches, he thought every old woman was a witch. Why, that man Murphy really felt sorry for Rhode Islanders for not hunting and punishing witches, and often he told them so.

Now, not far from his home there lived an old lady by the name of Becky Sims. She was always jolly and had a big laugh for everything, but that did not stop old Murphy from thinking her a witch. No, not him.

He was ever telling the harm she was doing to everyone and how once every month she rode to the witches' meeting. So often did he repeat this that in the end he was ready to swear that one time she even put a witch-bridle on him, riding him to a gathering where he had smelled burning sulphur and brimstone.

In the end he brought these charges against old Becky before the town's council.

"Well," said the eldest of the councilmen, "we don't believe you altogether, for we see no reason why witches should come to our state. You might have dreamt this after eating something bad. But, harken, we will punish her as a witch if you bring us a single proof that the old lady who is forever laughing is a witch. Go to her home and watch her; then come and tell us anything you see."

One afternoon the sky was black, the wind screamed, and lightning tore the air.

"A fine time for witch's work," cried old Murphy, and went to Becky Sims's house. He told her he was caught in the storm and please let him stay there until the storm was over.

"That you can, right gladly, goodman," she said cheerfully. "I always like to see a good neighbor in my home."

She was busy cleaning and getting ready ripe Rhode Island greening apples for a pie. The peeled apples looked like fresh white blossoms, and the smell of spices sweetened the whole room.

Old Murphy sat talking for hours and hours, talking about this and that. He was trying to see something that would prove her a witch. But all he got was the sweetest smell in the world of baking pie and Becky's chattering and laughing. Becky was bright as a new silver coin and guessed right well why old Murphy had come. But she never let on.

Well, it was getting on toward evening, the wind and the rain had died down, and Murphy was getting angrier every minute. Soon he would have to go, and not a thing had happened to prove Becky a witch.

A beautiful rainbow came up, and voices were heard outside. Some women who knew Murphy's errand had come to find out what had happened. Becky ran out to greet them, and Murphy decided there was no use waiting around longer. He got up and walked angrily toward the door, but the smell of the baking followed him like a silver moon in the dark, blue sky.

Quickly he turned around, went to the oven, opened it, took out the pie in the plate, covered it with a cloth he saw lying near, and put it inside of his shirt. But he forgot to close the oven door. Right then Becky and the neighbors came in. Now Becky had eyes sharper than a weasel's, and she quickly saw the open oven and that her pie was gone. She guessed at once just what had happened.

"Are you going so soon, good neighbor Murphy? Won't you stay for a piece o' pie and a cup o' milk with us?" she said sweetly.

"No, I'm in a hurry, mistress," said Murphy, for he began to feel the heat of the pie on his bare flesh.

He walked toward the door where old Becky stood. Said she:

"I just hate indeed to see such a fine friend as you go without eating. A happy day to you." And without further ado she threw her arms around him as hard as she could and embraced him.

At that old Murphy let out a fierce yell that could be heard as far as Providence. For Becky had squashed the steaming hot pie, and it ran out all over him inside of his shirt.

"So," screamed Goody Sims, "that's why you've been here all the noon, bothering me with your ceaseless blathering tongue—just to steal my pie! Out of here, you thief, and if ever again I see you in my house, I'll bring you before the judges."

Murphy ran out and kept on running for dear life, while the women screamed with laughter.

And that cured old Murphy of witch-hunting for the rest of his life. He never again accused Becky or any other woman of being a witch, not he. For he remembered the hot burning pie on his bare skin.

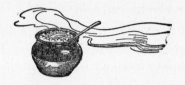

Grumpy Timothy Crumb

FAR back in the years there was a young fellow by the name of Timothy Crumb. Grumpy Tim they called him, and that was just the right name for him. Whatever happened didn't suit him, and everything he ever did went wrong—that's what he said. The more often he said it, the more grumpy he was and the more things went wrong, which is always the way. For when you think right, things go right, and when you think wrong, things go wrong.

One time he hired himself to Squire Chample, who had a lovely white-shingled house not far from Little Rest on the Chipauxet River. There he worked in wood and field, in barn and house, every day of the week except Sunday. Then he went to church and saw Sally Brown, Deacon Brown's pretty daughter. She had blue eyes and red hair, and she was round and soft and rosy. He liked Sally, and Sally said she could like him, too, if only he weren't so grumpy all the time, would smile once a day and speak cheerfully to every third body'd greet him. Tim tried now and then to do these things for Sal, but most of the time he was still complaining, telling all the world in general and Rhode Island in particular that he had no luck at all and whatever he did went wrong.

One day he said to Sally, "Come Sunday, I'll take ye to church. Ye be ready in the great-room."

Replied Sally:

"I'll be waiting for you, Tim, when you come. Only bring a smile with you and don't look so grumpy."

"I'll try, I'll try, Sal, seein' it's you that's askin', and it's the Lord's day. Honest, Sal, I'd be smilin' all the time, only things are forever goin' wrong, so I've nothin' to smile about."

"Hard luck don't follow people who are cheerful. Remember that, Tim."

"I'll remember," said Tim.

Sunday morning the sun shone bright and warm, and the flowers smelled sweet. Grumpy Tim got up and did the chores, grumbling all the time. Then he ate a big breakfast, doing a little more grumbling, and since there was plenty of time left he went to the creek to bathe so's he would be really shiny and clean when he'd meet Sally.

First he took off his bright red shirt and hung it on a swamp blueberry bush, since it was kind of wet and needed drying. Next he took off his shoes and put them under the bush.

"Bet that water is freezin' cold jest because I want to bathe," he grumbled. "I'd better see first."

So he walked in stocking feet, barebacked, toward the creek to see if the water wasn't too cold.

He didn't hear the birds' gay singing, nor did he see the flying squirrels leaping from branch to branch. He was too busy swatting flies that were zooming around his bare back. He didn't smell the sweet shrubs, and he didn't even see the giant swamp oak standing like a king along the creek. Nor did he see Old Wrinkle, Deacon Brown's brown and white bull, that was standing on a knoll not far from the creek. The deacon called him Old Wrinkle because the bull had a way of wrinkling his forehead like an old man.

Now Wrinkle, like most bulls, did not like red things. It made no difference to him whether it was a red shirt or a red blanket or a red petticoat, he just didn't like red in any form at all. No sooner did Wrinkle see Grumpy Tim's red shirt on the blueberry bush than he began running toward it angrily. He got hold of it, flung it on the green grass, and began tramping on it.

When Tim saw that, he made a dash to save his good red shirt, never giving a thought to the angry bull. But that angry bull gave all his thoughts to Tim when he saw him coming his way, for he liked a grumpy face as little as he liked a red shirt. He bent his head low down, nearly closed his little blazing eyes, and made a fierce dash for Grumpy Tim.

Tim wasn't easily scared, but he knew Old Wrinkle

weighed over a thousand pounds, and he was a little fellow and weighed just one hundred and eighteen pounds. So he decided to run back to the brook as fast as his legs would carry him.

Run he did, the bull after him, getting nearer all the time. Into the creek Tim ran, in his stockings. Now he could almost feel the beast's hot breath on his bare back. There was only one thing to save him from being trampled: to climb the big swamp oak standing at the edge of the creek. Quickly he got hold of a thick branch hanging low and swung himself on it. Up and up he went until he felt he was safe from Wrinkle, who stood under the tree bellowing, snorting, and pawing in wild fury.

You can just imagine how Grumpy Tim felt.

"Jest my luck; jest my luck. I kin never do anythin' but git into trouble." Right then he happened to be looking up in the branches over his head and what should he see but a hornets' nest big as a bushel basket, all covered with black hornets making ready to attack him! Grumpy Tim's eyes widened like saucers; he already felt black hornet stingers, sharp as knives, digging into his bare back.

"Jest my luck," he cried wildly as the buzzing of the hornets came nearer and nearer while the bull underneath was roaring and bellowing louder and louder.

Tim thought quickly and decided the bull's back wouldn't be half so bad as the hornets' stings.

Down he slid like a flash, landing on Old Wrinkle's

neck, and seized his horns with an iron grip. The bull couldn't understand what struck him. He turned his head to see, and two fistfuls of hornets landed on his wet nose and began stinging and stabbing him.

Some also landed on Tim's back, digging their stingers deep into his flesh.

Old Wrinkle saw all the world a-red, and he raced through the meadow, kicking wildly and snorting fire and roaring thunder. He kept on running and bellowing until he reached the chestnut rail fence that faced the barn and Deacon Brown's house. It was a neat little white house all covered with tall red hollyhocks, honeysuckle, and climbing roses. But neither Wrinkle nor Grumpy Tim saw the beauty of the flowers. Both roared in pain and anger louder than ever.

Sally was sitting all dressed in church clothes, bought in a "quality" store in Providence, waiting, when she heard the terrible noise. She ran out to see what it was all about.

It was just when Old Wrinkle lowered his head almost to the ground and made one desperate leap to reach his barn. He crashed through the chestnut rail fence and flung Tim high in the air. Wrinkle reached the barn, but Tim turned twice over, landing right on Sal, who was standing bewildered in her new store-bought clothes and bonnet.

Deacon Brown had also run out at the noise, and, seeing the half-dressed Tim and his daughter on the ground, began shouting with anger and rushed to get a stick. But hardly had he turned around than Grumpy Timothy Crumb leaped up and ran for dear life.

No one saw him in Rhode Island from that day on, but a tin-pan peddler from Connecticut who came by one day said he'd seen him in Hartford, still running away from hard luck. And what's happened to him I'll tell you when Grumpy Timothy Crumb has stopped running.

The Weaver-Woman's Monument

IN the Narragansett Country there once lived a weaver-woman, and some said she was a witch. What can one do with people who are so silly!

Everybody said she was a witch except God's own servant, the minister. He said she was a good woman, and some day the Lord would prove it in His own way. Did it help any? Not a bit. He preached himself hoarse on Sundays, and on other days the people called the weaver-woman a witch just the same.

But that did not stop them from asking her to weave their flax and wool. For there wasn't a finer, better, and faster weaver in all the land than the weaver-witch-woman of Rhode Island.

On a spring day, in the warm spring sunshine, she came to the home of Mistress Porter to weave and to spin and sat down at the spinning wheel. Thyrr! ckckck! bang! bang! the treadle began to spin faster than a swallow in flight. But soon the whirling and clacking

256

stopped and the weaver-woman just sat silently, staring into space, never moving foot or finger. She sat there a long, long time. Then of a sudden she began again. The treadle went faster than a falling star. Never did she stop for a second until the clapping sounded like a hundred mills going all at one and the same time.

When she was gone that night everybody in the Porter house still heard the whirring and clapping as if the treadle were going all the time.

The next morning the weaver-woman came back, and in the end she had a pile of cloth woven that three weavers couldn't do in that time.

"One person could never do that alone.—That clacking and whirring heard at night are evil spirits helping her.—She never speaks to a Christian soul.—She never asks for food or drink.—She's surely a witch and should be drowned as they do in other places," said evil tongues.

But the minister scolded them and said:

"She is no witch. No evil spirits help her at all. She is a sweet body and does not gossip, and that's the best way to get work done properly. The noise you hear at night is only in your head from hearing it all day long. I tell you that she is no witch, and some day God'll tell it to you in his own words."

That silenced the talkers but didn't stop them from thinking.

On a summer's day, on a sunny summer's day, young Porter, riding high on his horse, passed by the weaver-woman's little house. She was cutting flowers along the hedge while the bees sang all around her. Not a bee stung her, for bees do no harm to one who does no harm to them. Young Porter rode by without greeting or smile, swinging his whip in the warm air. He kept right on swinging the whip until he angered the bees and they stung him so hard he screamed with pain.

"It's the witch-weaver-woman who has sent these bees to sting me," he cried when he came to town. "She's a witch, and she should be burned."

"She's no witch at all," the minister again cried stoutly. "A bee stung you as bees often do. You leave the bees in peace, and they will not bother you."

In the golden fall, in the rainy fall, the weaver-woman sat in the loom loft of the mayor of the town, spinning and spinning pure white flax. She worked swift and fast, for there was a cold nip in the air and no stove in the room.

She worked so fast, she didn't know a fire broke out in the kitchen below. Everybody ran, but the weaver-woman was forgotten in the loom loft.

When she smelled the smoke, she hobbled slowly down the loft ladder, for she was a little woman, all bent and weak.

"Well, I'm glad everyone is out of the burning building," said the master of the house, a little ashamed for forgetting the weaver-woman.

The weaver-woman looked all around her.

"Not everyone is out of the house," she cried. "I saw Tabby, the old cat, up in the loft. She'll surely burn."

No one stirred. So she ran back into the house and soon stumbled out, nearly choked to death, with the cat under her arm.

"Only a witch would run into a burning building for an old black cat," cried those who were there. "We want no witches in our town."

"The weaver-woman is no witch at all," cried the minister on Sunday from the pulpit. "She is better than all of you. She risked her very life to save a poor animal. Some day God'll tell it to you so you'll never forget."

The wintry winds blew, the sharp snow came, and the weaver-woman was very sick. The smoke she had breathed in the burning house had hurt her lungs. It was hard to keep warm in her little wooden house, and no one came to help her.

"Since no man comes to help the poor old woman," said the Lord, "I will take her to me where she will need no help from any man."

So He took her to Him where there is neither cold nor suffering from the weather or from mankind.

The people found the little weaver-woman's body cold and shriveled, lying on her mattress of barley straw, and they wouldn't give her a decent Christian burial. The minister pleaded. But no stone or monument or cross was put on the earth to show where she was laid to rest.

"A witch she was," they cried, "and a witch needs no decent burial."

"You are cruel," said the minister sadly, "and some day God'll tell it to you, and you'll remember it."

The people jeered and broke the windows and doors of the weaver-woman's little house.

None came near the broken-down hut, only the sun and the moon, the rain, and the stars, who know no cruelty.

So spring came again, and summer, and the golden autumn.

One day the minister passed by the forlorn little house where the weaver-woman had lived. He went in, and there he saw a sight fit for Paradise, fit for angels. In the empty room, among the broken walls, lay the old, gray, torn mattress on which the old weaver-woman had died. But it looked neither torn nor gray. It was a beautiful sight. From the gray torn hemp sprouted golden-green mouse barley so that it was a joy to see.

The minister ran into town and brought the people back with him.

"Those are God's words," he cried pointing to the lovely flowers, "to tell you the weaver-woman was no witch. No flowers would grow where a witch lay. The golden grains on the cover are the Lord's own monument for one who was kind and good. So says the Lord, and you must never forget it."

The people felt in their hearts that the good minister was right, and they didn't forget it.

Little Annie
and the Whaler Captain

THE whales of the world had gathered in the ocean deep, right before America. They were seeking a way to get rid of their worst enemies, the whalers, who were forever hunting them for their whale oil.

There were giant whales, big as mountains, and less big whales, a little bigger than ships, and still less big ones, about twice as big as grown-up elephants. For even baby whales are very big.

A big white bull whale spoke first. He told about fierce Captain Munroe of Newport, Rhode Island, in America, who had caught more whales than any captain that ever sailed a whaling ship. If they could only stop him they wouldn't have to worry about the rest of the whalers in the world.

Each whale had a different idea about how it should be done. In the end all agreed that the best thing was to put a bell around the ship or better still around the captain. Just as the mice in the fairy tale tried to do to the cat. Then they'd hear him coming from afar. The only question was, who would hang the bell?

The white waves rocked high as church steeples, the fish swam through the waters, and the whales threw water spouts in the air, but not a single word was spoken. Of a sudden a voice was heard. It was Little Annie, a big baby whale.

"I can't get a bell from a sunken ship and hang it around Captain Munroe's neck, but I can do something better that'll put an end to his hunting us," she said.

The whales were stumped when the baby whale spoke so bold, and before they could say a word Little Annie, the big baby whale, swam off into the vast ocean, into the deep sea, to find fierce Captain Munroe. She swam up to the North Pole and then way down south. She mosied around ports and harbors until one fine day she spied the fierce Rhode Island captain and his bully crew. They were sailing along, not far from the shores of America, to catch the whales that floated in the salty waters.

On the boat, the spanker spanked and jib sail jibbed and Captain Munroe was a-singing:

"A smart Yankee boat lay out in the bay,
A smart Yankee boat lay out in the bay,
She was waiting for the wind to get under way,
She was waiting for the wind to get under way.

And, bully boys, we got that fair wind and we're in

luck. We'll make the greatest catch ever made by an American whaler between Baffin Bay an' the China Sea."

Right then, Clamface Jake, who sat in the crow's-nest a-looking for whales, roared, "Thar she blows! Thar she blowwws!"

The men ran for the boats, but Little Annie swam right up to the ship, swishing her tail in the foamy waves, a-blowing high water spouts.

"By the waters of Babylon! I think that she-whale is laughing right into my face," roared Captain Munroe, who looked like a whiskered walrus. "I'll harpoon that daughter of the briny sea right here from this deck. I'll teach her to make sport of an American whaling captain from Little Rhody."

He raised the sharp-pointed harpoon tied to the whale line and roared:

> "One-ery, two-ery, ickery Anne,
> So says my little Sally Anne,
> One, two, three!"

Then he flung the steel with all his might.

When Little Annie heard the captain a-roaring and saw the steel a-flying, she sang back:

> "Oh, Reuben Ranzo was no sailor,
> So he shipped aboard a Yankee whaler.
> He washed his face just once a fortnight,
> He said it was his nicest birthright."

She swung to the side, opened her mouth, and caught the harpoon between her teeth.

"Ho, fierce Captain Munroe," Little Annie squealed between her teeth. "Now we'll play a little game of ring-around-a-rosy."

"I'll give ye plenty of line and play my own little game," roared the whaler captain.

Little Annie laughed and held tight to the harpoon. She swam in a big circle until she felt the tug of the boat at the other end. First she tossed it larboard, next she swung it starboard, then she swam in great big circles, swifter than dolphins, swifter than flying fish.

"Ho, what kind of a game is this?" howled the captain. He didn't like this new kind of playing.

Instead of swimming over the rolling waves or down the briny sea, as whales have ever done, Little Annie swam in round large circles, singing:

> "Ring-a-round-a-rosy,
> A pocket full of posies,
> All fall down."

And when it came to "down," she'd give the ship a fierce tug that shivered its timbers and shook its boom.

"Play fair, pull straight," bellowed Captain Munroe.

But Little Annie only went faster. It was a sheer wonder to see the big baby whale swishing through the ocean like a streak of lightning, with the ship scudding swiftly through the air, round and round.

Poor Captain Munroe and his bully crew grew dizzy

in their heads. They thought they saw ships coming
from all sides and schools of whales shooting at them
like cannon balls.

> "Ring-a-round-a-rosy,
>   A pocket full of posies,
>   All fall down,"

sang Little Annie, the big baby whale, racing around
and around.

The captain and his crew grew dizzier and dizzier.
They were spinning on top of the waves faster than a
hurricane wind, and they saw a wall of ships around
them. The first was coming nearer and nearer! It was
just a boat's length from them, sails full a-flying!

"Stop or we'll crash," roared the frightened captain.

"It's the end," groaned the bully crew.

Little Annie went faster and faster! The other ship
was getting nearer and nearer.

"Stop, for my wife's and children's sake," pleaded
Captain Munroe. "If we crash I'll lose home and board."

"Promise you'll never go a-whaling again," sang out
Little Annie.

"I promise that and more besides. Only stop the ships
from crashing."

Then and only then did Little Annie, the big baby
whale, let the harpoon out of her teeth.

At once the ship they thought was coming toward
them fell farther and farther away. For it wasn't another

ship at all. It only seemed like one, because their own ship was racing round and round in circles.

The captain saw that he was tricked, but a whaling captain's word is as good as gold.

From that day on, Captain Munroe never went a-whaling. He tended sheep and cows on his farm. And so he lived happy ever after, he and his wife and his children, on their farm in Newport, in Rhode Island, in America.

As for Little Annie, the big baby whale, from then on she was the most beloved baby whale in all the oceans. For hadn't she got rid of the worst enemy of the whales? And in such a nice, nice, way. Just by playing,

> "Ring-a-round-a-rosy,
> A pocket full of posies,
> All fall down."

The Tale of Godfrey Malbone

IN those days, in the early days, there lived in Newport by the sea the merchant prince Godfrey Malbone. He was a big man, this Godfrey Malbone, and a proud man, and a rich man.

"Big!" he'd roar. "I'm big as the faith for which this plantation stands, the first settlement in America that truly carried out the great ideal of freedom for all. Any man can worship God as he wills, and he's welcome in Rhode Island as a brother. Our seal says, 'Love is all powerful.' "

"Proud! I've a right to be proud," he'd cry. "I've built a merchant empire with my own hands and brain, and now there's no man in the world I fear."

"Rich! I'm the richest merchant in Rhode Island by the sea," he'd shout. "Two hundred trading and privateering ships cover the ocean wide with my name and bring me wealth I cannot count. There's nothing, nothing in this big world, my money can't buy."

Those were his words, and, to show that he meant it,

267

he wrote them down and posted them publicly for all to read.

"There's nothing in the world my money won't buy," it said in big black letters on white paper.

Now there lived in Newport young Peleg, who carved beautiful heads to head brave ships that sailed the ocean wide. He was not a big fellow, but he was big in understanding. So, quietly one day, when no one was near, he put right underneath Godfrey Malbone's challenging words:

"There's nothing in the world my money won't buy," these words:

> "All the money in the place,
>   Will not buy Malbone a handsome face."

For you must know that old Malbone had a face homely enough to stop a clock. When Godfrey Malbone saw this, he ranted and swore and threatened and roared:

"I can't put horns on hares, but I can outsmart, out-eat, outdrink, outtrick any merchant alive. My face is the face of a man and not that of a whining ninny. Any man who'll tell me the name of the scoundrel who wrote these dastardly words, I'll give ten new golden guineas. I'll make that scoundrel look like a jellyfish pounded in a hard gumwood mortar."

The next day there was a grand feast in Godfrey Malbone's rich, large home, built like a courthouse for human justice. There were present, captains from ships come from long voyages, merchants, judges, soldiers, and friends, big as Godfrey Malbone and almost as rich.

Twenty-seven courses were served, cooked with rare spices. Every kind of wine, beginning with ports from Spain and Portugal, graced the table. And in between the eating and drinking there was big talk of great deeds with tales of feats of strength on the wild ocean.

Now the wine was served in silver goblets, but the food was served on plain, white plates. When a course was done, Godfrey Malbone would sing a song in a roaring voice and at the end would break the plate from which he had eaten. Captains and guests joined the chorus and smashed the plates as well.

"Ha!" cried the jolly host with red steaming face. "It saves washing in the kitchen and gives the poor plate makers of Old England a chance to earn a little more money from me. What won't my money buy? Again I cry, ten shiny guineas for the one who tells me the name of the dog who wrote the scurvy rhyme under my words."

Right then, there came a cry of "Fire! Fire in the kitchen!" Cooks and servants rushed out wildly while big flames began leaping out of the fifty-foot-long room where Godfrey Malbone's food was cooked.

Guests and host rushed out, too. They took along two big red-running roasts, three sweet-smelling hams, seven bronze-breasted turkeys, a calf's leg, a mountain of corn bread and mince pies, with buckets and bottles of rich wines.

There was crying and screaming and a wild to-do, but all to no avail. The fine white-pillared house was burning high, yellow, and smoky. The brisk west wind made the flames dance in the air like ragged autumn leaves.

Roared Godfrey Malbone, "What a fine sight! Nero saw no better when Rome was burning. But while the heathen king could only think of fiddling, I would rather think of good eating. Come, captains and gentlemen, come, all of ye. Let us sit under this old buttonwood tree and eat and drink and be merry. Ho, there! Serve the meal under the tree," he said to his servants.

Soon they sat around the old tree as if nothing were amiss. It was a wondrous sight to see. There amidst dark green boxwood, red roses, larkspur, yellow flag, pinks, and other flowers arranged in fine design near a little pond of silver fish, sat this grand company of big Rhode Islanders. They sat eating, drinking, and singing in the light of the red sun and the yellow leaping flames of the burning house.

People came from far and from near, drawn by the high flames and the smoke, wanting to help, but Godfrey Malbone shouted:

"Don't disturb us at our meal. Let my house burn to cinders. My money'll build me a new one soon enough. Ha! What won't my money buy! Remember, captains, gentlemen, and people of the town, ten fine golden guineas to the one who tells me who wrote the slandering rhyme about me."

A young fellow, smiling pleasantly, stepped forth from the crowd. It was Peleg, the carver. He said quietly:

"Master Malbone, I claim the ten golden guineas."

"But first I want to know the name of the rascal who wrote the scurrilous rhyme," said Malbone.

"Why, it was none other than me, sir," replied Peleg.

There was a dead silence among the grand company and among the townspeople. Godfrey Malbone's face turned purple. The knuckles of his balled fists were white. Rising from his seat he walked up to where Peleg stood smiling and quiet. He raised his heavy fists high and then . . . his hands dropped slowly to his sides. On his big, ugly face there came first a twitching at the corners of his mouth, then a slow grin, then a big, hearty, roaring laugh. The company looked at this first in speechless surprise and then joined in the good laughter.

Shouted Godfrey Malbone:

"By God! It's only a little man who can't laugh when the joke's on him. Peleg, you young scamp, sure as the Lord made little apples, you're right and deserve the ten golden guineas. Here they are and come join us in our feast. Only, remember, 'twas the good Lord gave me my face, and so it can't be ugly altogether."

Peleg sat down, and all the people cheered Godfrey Malbone so that the angels heard it in the sky. For there was a real man! a big man, a generous man, one who loved happy laughter so much he could laugh at himself.

From that day on, Peleg, the carver, and Godfrey Malbone, the merchant prince, became the best of friends, and never again did the latter brag that money could buy everything.